Deadly Encounters:
How Infectious Disease Helped Shape Australia

**Peter Curson** is an Honorary Professor of Population and Security at Sydney University and Emeritus Professor of Population and Health at Macquarie University. With a background, in Historical Demography, Public Health and Geography he is particularly interested in the links between infectious disease and human behaviour. He is the author of 12 books, more than 130 academic papers and 160 radio and TV programs and has written extensively on epidemics and pandemics in Australian history. He is also a regular contributor to the Australian and New Zealand media.

**By the same author:**

*A Time of Terror. The Black Death in Sydney.* Xlibris, 2022.

*Border Conflicts in a German Southern African Colony*: Jakob Morengo and the Untold Tragedy of Edward Presgrave, Arena Books, 2012.

*Plague Anatomy: Health Security from Pandemics to Bioterrorism*, Strategy Monograph ASPI.2005 [with B.McRandle]

*Global Environmental Crises* [Joint editor]. OUP, 1999.

*Climate Change and Human Health in the Asia Pacific Region* [Joint Editor]. AMA/Greenpeace, 1997.

*Plague in Sydney: The Anatomy of an Epidemic.* UNSW Press, 1989 [with K.McCracken].

*Population and Disasters* [Joint Editor and contributor of 3 chapters]. Blackwells, 1989.

*Times of Crisis: Epidemics in Sydney 1788-1900.* Sydney University Press, 1985.

# Deadly Encounters

How Infectious Disease Helped Shape Australia

**Peter Curson**

**Arena Books**

Copyright © 2015, 2024, Peter Curson

The right of Peter Curson to be identified as author of this book
has been asserted in accordance with the Copyright, Designs and
Patents Act 1988.

First published by Arena Books in 2015
Second edition published by Arena Books in 2024

www.arenabooks.co.uk

Peter Curson

***Deadly Encounters:*** *How infectious disease helped shape Australia*

A CIP catalogue record for this Book is available from the British Library.

ISBN: 978-1-914390-25-8 Paperback
ISBN: 978-1-914390-26-5 Ebook

Thema: MJCJ; MBX; NHTF.


Cover design by Arena Books

# CONTENTS

# LIST OF FIGURES

# LIST OF TABLES

# LIST OF PLATES

**Plate 1.1:** S.S. Zealandia, 1913. Photograph by Henry Allport. With thanks to the State Library of Tasmania.

**Plate 1.2:** Crew of S.S. Zealandia undergoing quarantine inspection at Freemantle after leaving Sydney in 1913. Crew includes the 3rd class steward responsible for the smallpox outbreak in New South Wales. Source: Image PRG 280/1/16/86. Courtesy of the State Library of South Australia.

**Plate 1.3**: Official newspaper announcements re quarantine July 1913. Source: The Daily Mail, 5th & 7th July 1913, page 13 and page 9.

**Plate 1.4**: Quarantine Station at North Head, Sydney. Source: The Author.

**Plate 1.5:** North Head Sydney Quarantine Station buildings near wharf. Source: The Sydney Mail, 31st March 1900.

**Plate 1.6:** 28-year old male smallpox case admitted to Quarantine Station, in 10th day of efflorescence. Source: Robertson, 1914, No. 12.

**Plate 2.1:** "X" Disease Press release 1918. Source: Daily Telegraph, 12th February 1918, page 4.

**Plate 3.1:** "Breaking & Entering", James Case's cartoon of the struggle between the Acting Australian Prime Minister William Watt and the Queensland Government over Queensland's decision to unilaterally close its borders and institute formal quarantine in 1919. Courtesy of the National Archives of Australia.

**Plate 3.2:** Riley Street Influenza Depot, Sydney, nurses and staff. Source: Image dl_13498. Courtesy State Library of New South Wales.

**Plate 3.3:** Hospital beds in Great Hall, Melbourne Exhibition Building during the influenza pandemic of 1919. Source: Image MM103429, Courtesy of the Museum of Victoria.

**Plate 3.4:** Influenza inoculation at Hyde Park Depot and crowd at Inoculation Depot. Source: Sydney Mail, 5th February 1919, page 18.

**Plate 3.5:** Influenza Quarantine Camp, Jubilee Oval, Adelaide, 1919. Source: Photograph PRG 280/1/15/432. Courtesy of the State Library of South Australia.

**Plate 3.6:** Chamberlain's Cough Remedy. Source: The Bulletin, February 1919.

**Plate 4.1:** Dengue Mosquito, Aedes Aegypti. Source: ID9261. Courtesy CDC Public Health Image Library & F.H. Collins.

**Plate 4.2:** ASPRO and DENGUE advertisement, 1926. Source: Maryborough Chronicle, Wide Bay and Burnett Advertiser, 24th March 1926, page 3.

**Plate 4.3:** FLY-TOX advertisement, 1926. Source: The Brisbane Courier, 1st April 1926, page 12.

**Plate 4.4:** Australian Dengue fever poster, 1940s. Source: Image MO742/1. Courtesy of the National Archives of Australia.

**Plate 5.1:** Young polio child on crutches at Margaret Reid Hospital, New South Wales Society for Crippled Children, St. Ives, Sydney. Source: Image d_707311. Courtesy of the State Library of New South Wales.

**Plate 5.2:** Vaccination against polio at Randwick Girls School, Sydney. Source: Image d2_07705. Courtesy of the State Library of New South Wales.

**Plate 5.3:** Iron Lung, Royal North Shore Hospital, Sydney. Source: Image d_211851. Courtesy of the State Library of New South Wales.

**Plate 5.4:** Sister Elizabeth Kenny, pioneer of alternative Polio treatment. Source: Image hood_26494. Courtesy of the State Library of New South Wales.

**Plate 6.1:** Australian HIV/AIDS poster. Source: Image L0052679. Courtesy of the Welcome Library London and the Australian National Council on AIDS.

**Plate 7.1:** "PLAGUE FEAR Sars, superbugs and the coming winter," The New Zealand Listener, May 10-16, 2003, cover page. Courtesy of the New Zealand Listener/Bauer Media.

# ACKNOWLEDGEMENTS

This book has been long in the making. Initially conceived in the early 1990s during the heyday of the Climatic Impacts Centre at Macquarie University when the author was engaged in pioneering the study of the links between climate change and infectious disease, it has ultimately come together almost 30 years later. The author owes a debt to a number of researchers and postgraduates who offered support and helped gather material. In particular, mention should be made of Julia Porter for her help with the dengue research, Carolyn Greentree, Gail Hesselman and Tricia Thomson for assiduously sifting through mountains of archival information, and later at Sydney University, Rebekah Menzies for the work on HIV/AIDS. The author's interest in epidemics of infectious disease and human behaviour extends even further back. In the early 1980s he spent almost a year laboriously trawling through the 19th century parish registers of Sydney churches as well as through endless archival and newspaper records. In 1985 some of this material appeared in the book *Times of Crisis* but much has had to wait until this book. The environment at Macquarie during the period from 1985 until 2000 was extraordinarily involving and supportive. It was a time when Macquarie's reputation for studies in Medical and Population Geography was world renown as was the work of the Climatic Impacts Centre. One could have not asked for a more supportive and enlivening environment within which to pursue such research. The book was completed while I was at Sydney University in the Centre for International Security Studies. The period from 2007 until 2011 in the Centre was incredibly warm and supportive, and the environment conducive to high quality research. For this I thank the then Director Alan Dupont and Vivian his Executive Assistant. Christian Enemark also provided a good role model for high quality research into infectious disease for which I thank him. Mention must also be made of my cartographer Judy Davis for her fine work. The severe outbreak of COVID-19 which swept the world and Australia in 2020 and which lingers on today enouraged me to respond to a publisher's request for a new edition of Deadly Encounters Finally, I would like to thank my daughter Alisa for her invaluable help in proof reading and correcting the text as well as my beloved late wife Sheila for putting up with the preoccupation of an academic locked away in a room stacked with archival material from the 19th and 20th centuries.

# Introduction

Epidemics of infectious disease have been a deep-seated and inescapable part of Australian life since the first days of early settlement. Over the last 200 or so years the lives of many Australians have been swept up in outbreaks of infectious disease. Such episodes brought home the message that for many Australians infectious disease was an inescapable feature of the insecurity of everyday life and a regular reminder of the ubiquitous presence of death and disease. Although such epidemic encounters were often short-lived events and for the most part, not great demographic crises, they nonetheless had tremendous impact and their effects were wide ranging (Curson, 1985, p.168).

Reconstructing the past history of epidemic experience in Australia is important for a number of reasons. Firstly, while the epidemiological impact of such events, in terms of cases and deaths, was often limited, their psycho-social impact was tremendous. They captured public attention and were often responsible for great outpourings of fear, panic and hysteria. Secondly, they were often the catalyst of public health reform, particularly in the way they focused our attention on the significance of the biophysical and human environments, and where they directed our attention to the often unsanitary and impoverished living and working conditions that existed in many parts of Australia. Thirdly, they put to the test and challenged Commonwealth/ State/Local Governments' comprehension and management of extreme natural events and frequently found them wanting. Finally, they place in sharp perspective the internal workings of Australian society, in particular, stripping away the veneer that we erect around our lives, and revealing us as we truly are – fearful of infection and contagion, wary of "others" and "outsiders," anxious about threats from "outside", needing to find someone to blame, and often highly sceptical about the Governments' power and ability to protect us.

A full and comprehensive history of infectious disease in Australia remains to be written. Unlike Maclean's classic study of public health in New Zealand published more than 50 years ago, no such work exists in Australia (see Maclean, 1964). An earlier book on epidemic disasters in Sydney between 1788 and 1900 represented a small step in this direction (see Curson, 1985). Hopefully, this present book, which extends the analysis into the 20th and 21st centuries, will go part of the way to bridge this gap.

One of the interesting things to emerge from this study of epidemics of infectious disease in Australia over the last 100 years is the fact of how easily we are panicked by the threat of epidemic disease and how small a part knowledge of past epidemics plays in our historical memory. Our experience with SARS, Avian Flu, Swine Flu and now COVID-19, demonstrates this only too well. Australian history is in fact littered with major outbreaks of infectious disease and/or the threat of pandemics. Over the past 200 or so years Australia has been swept up in numerous pandemics, from scarlet fever and influenza in the early 19th century through bubonic plague, smallpox and influenza in the early 20th century, to HIV/AIDS from the 1980s and Swine Flu in the first two decades of the 21st century and finally, COVID-19 which continues to dominate our lives. The early years of the 20th century were particularly important for epidemic and pandemic outbreaks. The last great pandemic of bubonic plague which killed more than 30 million people worldwide claimed at least 535 lives in Australia between 1900 and 1925. The last pandemic of smallpox (variola minor) which affected the world between 1897 and 1940, affected Australia between 1913 and 1917, causing at least 3,000 cases in New South Wales. The influenza pandemic of 1918-19 probably killed about 15,000 people in Australia and remains one of the nation's greatest natural disasters. Australia has also experienced at least seven major outbreaks of dengue since 1897, the first three of which were major outbreaks. In 1904-05, for example, there were approximately 220 deaths in Queensland/Northern New South Wales during the epidemic and possibly well over 100,000 cases.

The greatest dengue epidemic in Australian history, however, occurred in 1925-26 when the disease extended from the northern most parts of Queensland, down the east coast almost to Sydney. In total there were probably more than 560,000 cases of dengue during the epidemic, including 147 deaths. It remains the greatest epidemic of a vector-borne disease in Australian history and its effects were wide-ranging. Polio also occupies a unique place in the history of infectious disease in Australia. It first appeared in the late 19th century and over the next 50 years became to be regarded with tremendous apprehension and fear. During the first half of the 20th century there were more than 32,000 cases of polio officially reported, but given that many cases of minor paralysis went unreported, the real number was well over 60,000. Until the mid 1950s, polio virtually held Australians hostage and engendered great outpourings of fear and dread. And what of HIV/AIDS possibly destined to become the most devastating epidemic in human history? Unlike the other infectious diseases examined HIV/AIDS is a slow viral disease with exposure and infection often taking up to a decade to fully reveal themselves. So far HIV/AIDS has affected more than 35 million people around the world including more than 32,000 in Australia. But in terms of cases and deaths, COVID-19 outstrips them all. So far, by late May 2023 11,700,577 COVID-19 cases and 21,877 deaths had occurred in Australia. The number of deaths clearly outclassing the number of Australians who died during the 1919 Flu pandemic.

But what exactly is an epidemic? We continue to use the term so casually and metaphorically in our everyday life and the media constantly refer to the epidemic of homelessness, the epidemic of violence and the epidemic of drug dealing. The term epidemic has acquired a particular meaning in the popular mind, something that comes from without, stays for a length of time and then disappears. The term epidemic lacks quantitative precision and in many ways an epidemic is determined by the temporal and spatial stage on which it plays out. For example, 25 cases of severe gastrointestinal disease aboard a small river cruiser over a period of 7 days, 40 cases of severe diarrhoea in a small retirement home over two weeks, 200 cases of Norovirus aboard a huge ocean cruise ship on a three week cruise, or 2,000 cases of dengue in a number of country towns over a three month period would all be classified as epidemics. But in most cases it is not simply the number of cases and deaths that defines an epidemic as much as the public reaction to the disease agent involved. SARS demonstrated that very well as where the actual number of cases and deaths was small, but the outpouring of human fear and emotion, huge. Our reaction to COVID-19 also demonstrated how people responded. For Rosenberg, epidemics have dramaturgic form. "They commence at a moment in time and proceed on a stage limited in space and duration and follow a plot line of increasing revelatory tension, move to a crisis of individual and collective character, then drift toward closure" (Rosenberg, 1992, p.279). There is little doubt that an epidemic is more than just a cluster of cases and deaths in time and space, but also involves important aspects of human reaction, response and behaviour, often manifesting in outpourings of fear, hysteria and panic.

Deadly Encounters

This book examines how Australian society reacted to a series of epidemic encounters that occurred in the period after 1910. All these epidemics were traumatic and defining events. The book documents the impact, diffusion and effects of these epidemic crises. By examining in some detail the impact of these traumatic events it is hoped to throw light on human behaviour in times of stress. Underlying the writer's approach is the assumption that there is a need for retrospective studies of the behaviour of epidemics in Australian history and how different populations exposed to a variety of devastating circumstances responded. There is also little doubt that close observation of the way people respond during times of crisis reveals much about social attitudes, patterns of activity and interaction, as well as revealing underlying tensions, conflicts and antagonisms that otherwise might remain hidden. In many cases the experience of such disease outbreaks resulted in significant changes in human values, attitudes and behaviour, leading to important changes in public health. There also remains much to be learned about the role played by human emotion, fear and hysteria during times of epidemic crisis. In each of these epidemics there were two distinctive components. In the first place, there was the physical manifestation of the disease revealed in the number of cases and deaths. In the second place, there was societies' often predictable reaction, revealed in outpourings of fear, hysteria and panic, which was far more widespread, and at times threatened to overwhelm the epidemiological impact. The final chapter in this book takes up this theme and looks in some detail at the nature of fear and human reaction, paying particular attention to the nature of risk and what role the media plays during times of epidemic crisis.

The significance of this book lies in the fact that it contributes to our understanding of the social construction of epidemics and the nature of human behaviour associated with such events. Relatively little is known about the way people behave during times of extreme crisis and in particular why they behave as they do. We also need to know much more about how people regard risk and personal vulnerability, and in particular in the words of Darnton, to understand "how they structure the world in which they live, invest it with meaning and infuse it with emotion" (Darnton, 1984, p.3). At a broader level we also need more information about the socio-psychological climate surrounding the passage of epidemics, particularly the panic, fear and hysteria engendered, as well as the scapegoating and how various players such as the media and business manipulate such fear for their own purposes. One of the greatest values in studying epidemics is that they allow us to close with much greater precision on the details of everyday life. In this sense, epidemics act as mirrors or magnifying glasses, reflecting and illuminating basic social divisions and conflicts that under more normal circumstances might remain

4

hidden. Consequently, epidemics constitute a unique laboratory for the study of individual and group behaviour during times of great stress. A part of this book is also interested in exploring how governments and medical authorities reacted to these crises and how the management and control procedures that they put into place impacted upon the community at large.

One of the great ironies of Australia's public health is that many of the lessons learned from epidemic encounters over the last 200 years were soon lost and forgotten as Australia lurched from one epidemic crisis to another. In the final analysis, it seems clear that if we do not learn from the past and simply dismiss what happened as part of an earlier less scientific age, we run the risk of repeating the mistakes made. As Ashburton-Thompson, possibly Australia's greatest public health practitioner remarked in 1899, "The brilliancy of modern discoveries blinds incautious eyes to old truths and often endangers sound practice" (Ashburton-Thompson, 1899, p.491). In the case of the history of epidemics in Australia nothing could be closer to the truth. We have much to learn from how our fellows in time and space responded to such crises.

A number of crucial messages emerge from this study. In the first place we need to appreciate that the hope of an infectious disease - free age so triumphantly proclaimed over 30 years ago, has proved to be illusionary. Epidemics and pandemics are no longer a thing of the past and over the last 30 years infectious disease has returned to the international agenda with the emergence of so-called "new" infections and the persistence of older infections once thought to be under control. Hardly a month goes by now without the report of the emergence of some new microbiological threat to human health and wellbeing. In the second place there is little doubt that we have severely under-estimated the significance of the biophysical environment and the role that it plays in our lives. The microbial world is ever-changing and adapting not only to its natural environment but also to changes in the behaviour of its animal and human hosts. There is also little doubt that we need to better understand how we react and behave during times of severe crisis, how we evaluate risk and vulnerability in our lives, what role fear and anxiety play in our lives, and how our reactions are influenced by government decisions and by the way the media presents such events to us. Hopefully, this book will go some way to addressing some of these important issues.

CHAPTER 1

# The Return of an Old Pestilence: The Smallpox Epidemic of 1913-1917

Smallpox occupies an important place in the history of infectious disease in Australia. Outbreaks occurred on at least 15 occasions between 1789 and 1917. With the exception of epidemics in 1789, 1829-45, 1881-82, 1887, 1903 and 1913-17, most involved only a handful of cases and were limited in their geographical extent. The reaction that such outbreaks engendered in the population was, however, out of all proportion to the number of cases and deaths produced.

In 1913 an epidemic of smallpox broke out in Sydney – the first outbreak of this dreaded disease in the city for almost 30 years. The disease seems to have been introduced to the city by a 3rd Class steward aboard the S.S. Zealandia that arrived in Sydney from Vancouver via Honolulu, Suva and Auckland on the 12th of April (Plates 1.1 and 1.2). At the time the ship sailed from Vancouver, smallpox had been widespread in British Columbia for a number of months. It would appear that the steward, who fell ill towards the end of the journey while the ship was in Suva, had the responsibility for attending to a number of Mormon missionaries en route from Utah to New Zealand. Two days out of Vancouver, one of the missionaries developed a pustular rash, but the disease was mild and he soon recovered. Seven days after disembarking at Auckland, however, while attending a Hui or Maori tribal gathering near Whangarei, his cabin mate from the voyage became ill, developed a pustular rash and subsequently infected most of the household with whom he was staying. Ultimately he would be responsible for spreading the infection to a widespread Maori community across the Auckland Province from Mangonui in the north to the Waikato in the south. Initially confined to remote rural Maori communities, the disease also affected those living in small towns such as Kaikohe. Because of the mildness of the disease it would seem that many cases went unreported. By early 1914, a total of almost 2,000 Maoris had succumbed to smallpox as well as 116 Europeans. All in all, 55 Maoris died during the epidemic (See Buck, 1914). By the time the steward on the Zealandia arrived in Sydney, he was in a mild eruptive phase of the disease, with pimples on his face and neck. He did not believe his illness was serious enough to consult the ship's surgeon and simply dismissed it as a "crop of boils". On disembarkation in Sydney, he was still suffering from this condition. As far as can be ascertained, no other person on the Zealandia caught the disease.

On arrival in Sydney, the steward went to his mother's house where he entertained his girlfriend. Over subsequent days, he saw more of this girl who worked in an undergarment factory in Chalmers Street. During this time he continued to suffer from a pustular rash on his face. More than a month later in late May 1913 the full impact of these social meetings would become apparent, when the owner and manager of an underclothing factory in Chalmers Street Sydney, noticed that a number of his female employees had reported sick over the previous few weeks with a mild infective rash resembling a crop of pimples. Many of the girls reported that their rash had been preceded by a mild respiratory illness accompanied by headaches, backache, shivering and general pains. A number took a few days off from work and then returned to work. On the last day of May, one of the factory girls was admitted to the Coast Hospital at Little Bay suffering from a widespread rash covering much of her body. Seen by medical staff, her condition was diagnosed as chickenpox. On the same day, a young female employee from a clothing factory in Kent Street, who was a friend of the steward's girlfriend, fell ill at her home in Granville, with a pustular rash covering most of her face, trunk and limbs. Again, because of the mildness of the infection, her case was diagnosed as chickenpox. Almost three weeks later, the Sydney Hospital notified the Public Health Department of a young girl admitted with a copious rash, which for all ostensible purposes resembled smallpox. This and the earlier cases of "chickenpox," were now regarded with suspicion, and a number of the girls originally diagnosed as suffering from chickenpox were encouraged to return to the Department of Public Health and undergo vaccination under controlled circumstances. Four days later it became apparent that all those previously diagnosed as chickenpox had failed to respond to the vaccination, and the

Board of Health reported to the Premier that the disease was in fact, smallpox. Eleven weeks had transpired since the Zealandia had berthed in Sydney and the Third Class steward had entertained his girlfriend.

Once introduced to Sydney, the disease spread beyond the city to many country areas and rural towns, and remained a threat for almost five years. Officially, only 2,400 cases and four deaths were notified, the majority in Sydney, but it seems clear that a large number of cases went unreported, and by the time the disease was officially recognized in Sydney, it is possible that the epidemic was at its peak. If this was the case, then it is possible that upwards of 3,000 people actually caught smallpox including at least 2,000 in Sydney alone. This outbreak of smallpox was important for a number of reasons. In the first place it was a relatively benign form of the disease, with very low infectivity and mortality, which spread widely over New South Wales, and persisted for almost five years. In the second, it produced a bitter clash between the Commonwealth and State Government over quarantine procedures and public health controls. Thirdly, despite the small number of cases and deaths and the relatively mild nature of the infection, the outbreak initially gave rise to great scenes of panic, fear and hysteria. In the middle months of 1913 there was, for example, a stampede to get vaccinated and hundreds of cases and suspected cases were forcibly removed from their homes and incarcerated at the Quarantine Station at North Head. Much of inner Sydney was officially declared "infected" and formally quarantined. Controls were placed on the movement of people, goods and mail. Many small businesses "went to the wall", families were split up, and homes demolished. Finally, the epidemic ignited once again, the compulsory vaccination controversy that had marked New South Wales life at least since the latter part of the previous century. To those Sydneysiders who had lived through the smallpox epidemic of 1881-82 and the plague epidemics in the earlier part of the 20th century, this was history repeating itself (see Curson, 1985).

## The Variola Minor Pandemic of 1897-1940s

The epidemic of smallpox that broke out in Sydney in 1913 and lingered in the State until the latter part of 1917, was part of the world pandemic of Variola Minor that first came to world attention when it appeared in the USA towards the end of the 19th century.

In November 1897, an epidemic of smallpox broke out in the Florida city of Pensacola in the Gulf of Mexico and soon spread beyond the city limits to the surrounding countryside. Probably introduced from Southern Africa, the disease was distinctive in so far as none of those affected died, and it soon became clear that while physically the disease resembled the classical smallpox of old; in reality it was a much milder form of the disease. This was the first recorded outbreak of Variola Minor in North America, and it ushered in a period when the disease would become pandemic around the world. Within a few years the disease spread across much of the USA and reached Canada and later Europe. What distinguished this disease from the smallpox which had afflicted the world for centuries, was its very low mortality, its low infectivity rate and the fact that many of those infected developed a much milder illness with far less of the scarring afterwards. Given such symptoms it is not surprising that the disease was frequently misdiagnosed as chickenpox. Variola Minor was to remain the predominant form of smallpox in North America and Europe for at least the next three decades and was responsible for some substantial epidemics, particularly in cities like Boston, New York and Philadelphia.

The epidemic of Variola Minor that broke out in Sydney during 1913 was by all measures exceedingly mild. Generally, most people suffered a short period of high fever, accompanied by general malaise, headache and backache. Such symptoms usually abated after a few days, and thereafter, the patient generally suffered little discomfit. Within a few days, a mild eruption usually occurred, although in many cases the rash was scanty on the upper half of the body with often as little as three or four pocks. There were a number of cases where no rash or pocks developed at all. While the epidemic was generally very mild, some suffered more profuse symptoms more akin to classical smallpox, but such cases were few. Table 1.1 details the symptoms of 1,618 cases of smallpox treated at the Quarantine Station between 1 July 1913 and the 25th of March 1915. This data indicates the mildness of the epidemic. In almost half the total cases, the rash/eruptions were very mild, with an additional 4 percent suffering moderately severe symptoms. Only 4 percent of all cases suffered a severe form of eruptions or skin pocking.

**Table 1.1:** Nature of Smallpox Symptoms - of Cases Treated at Quarantine Station. 1 July 1913 – 25 March 1915, % in [ ]

| Severe/ Semi-Confluent Eruptions | Moderately Severe Rash/ Eruptions | Very Mild Rash Eruptions | Total |
|---|---|---|---|
| 68 [4.2] | 716 [44.2] | 772 [47.7] | 1618* |
| * 62 or 3.8% not stated | | | |
| Source of Data: Cumpston and McCollum, 1925, Table 19 | | | |

## The Course of the Epidemic

Table 1.2 indicates the number of cases of smallpox in New South Wales during the course of the epidemic. Between 1913 and 1918 there were 2,400 cases of smallpox officially notified, the majority occurring in 1913, with smaller outbreaks in subsequent years. Figure 1.1 illustrates the temporal progression of the epidemic in the 1913-15 period. What this figure suggests, is that by the time smallpox was officially declared in Sydney at the beginning of July and notification of cases began, the epidemic had already peaked. In other words, Figure 1.1 closely approximates just one side of an epidemic or normal curve with the left side of the distribution missing. Given that the Steward from the Zealandia was socially active in Sydney from mid April, and that smallpox affected many young people working in inner Sydney factories as well as others, it seems very likely that official records substantially understate the real numbers of cases in the epidemic. Figure 1.2 attempts to reconstruct the missing cases from the first three months of the epidemic, and postulates that approximately 450-500 cases took place before official notification began in early July. If this was truly the case, then the correct number of victims in the epidemic in Sydney in 1913 was probably nearer 2,000.

| **Table 1.2:** Smallpox Cases in New South Wales 1913 – 1918 | | | | | | |
|---|---|---|---|---|---|---|
| | **1913** | **1914** | **1915** | **1916** | **1917** | **Total** |
| **Sydney** | 1017 [1517]* | 445 | 41 | 16 | | 1519 [2019]* |
| **Hunter River District** | 1 | 44 | 411# | 33 | 14 | 503 |
| **Remainder NSW** | 55 | 139@ | 19 | 59^ | 105+ | 378! |
| **Total** | 1073 [1573]* | 628 | 471 | 108 | 119 | 2400 [2900]! |

| | |
|---|---|
| * | Includes author's estimate of unrecorded cases. |
| # | Includes: Cessnock 98; Hamilton 63; Wickham 60; Newcastle 47; Wallsend 35 |
| @ | Includes: Yass 20; Quirindi 20; Coolalie 17; Moree 15; Newcastle 15 |
| ^ | Includes: Narrabri 30 |
| + | Includes: Warren 66; Coonamble 14; Coonabarabran 13 |
| ! | Includes 1 case in 1918 |

Source: Author and Cumpston and McCallum, 1925

The epidemic commenced in mid April, reached a peak in July and thereafter slowly declined over the following four months. Between July and November, 959 cases or 63 percent of the total number occurred (or 1,450 if we include the missing April-July cases). During the epidemic, only four people were recorded as dying of smallpox. In the case of two of the deaths, smallpox was simply a secondary or contributing cause, as in the case of a 75 year old male suffering from advanced stomach cancer who was an inmate of the Hospice for the Dying. In the other case, a 23 year-old female caught smallpox while suffering from advanced Bright's disease, from which she died. Two persons probably died from the effects of smallpox. A 29 year-old female with semi-confluent smallpox, died a few hours after giving birth. The other, a 23 day–old infant, died from smallpox caught from his mother.

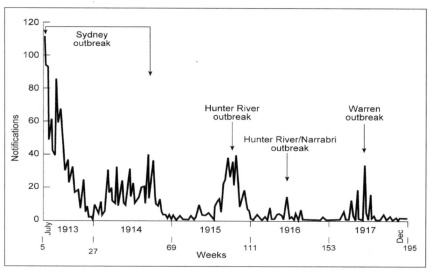

**Figure 1.1** Weekly Notifications of Smallpox Cases, New South Wales, 1913-17.

Geographically speaking, there was not one epidemic of smallpox between 1913 and 1918 but a number. In 1913-14, the epidemic was almost exclusively a Sydney affair, with approximately 70 per cent of all cases occurring with the Metropolitan area and its southern outskirts. Scattered cases did occur in country districts to the west and southwest of Sydney in these years, but in every case, these were the result of an infectious Sydney case travelling outside of Sydney (Figure 1.3). The most significant of these country outbreaks occurred at Yass in September 1914, where a number of railway workers engaged in work on the Yass- Coolalie deviation caught smallpox. The disease quickly spread to the nearby town of Yass, and ultimately resulted in 42 cases. All were treated in a temporary isolation hospital established at the railway camp. The impact that one infected patient could have in diffusing the disease around the State, was well illustrated in mid June 1914 when a Sydney barber who lived in St Peters and worked in Newtown, decided to take up a position with a hairdressing establishment in Moree in the far north of the State. Prior to departing for Moree, he was suffering from a mild respiratory complaint, which developed into a rash-like illness soon after his arrival in the town. Treated by the local chemist, he took a week off work during which time he lived in a local boarding house with a number of fellow tradesmen. Within a couple of weeks, all the inhabitants of the boarding house were ill with smallpox, as well as a number of visitors. Over the next week, the infection spread to involve 10 other people in the town. In total, 17 persons caught smallpox in Moree during June 1914. In 1915, a more significant epidemic broke out in the Newcastle and Hunter River District to the north of Sydney. Almost 60 per cent of the 411 cases occurred in the Newcastle urban area, but the epidemic also extended west and north-westwards to involve parts of the Cessnock Shire and Wallsend.

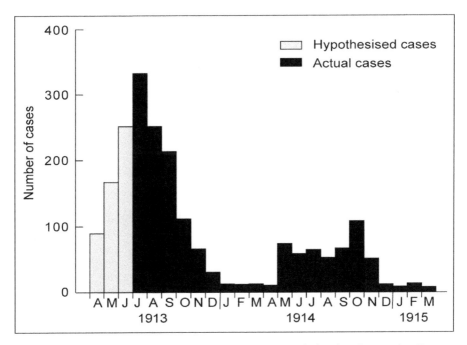

**Figure 1.2.** Monthly Distribution of Smallpox Cases Admitted to Quarantine Station, 1913-1915.

Alost 100 cases occurred in and around the Cessnock – Kurri Kurri and surrounding area. Most cases were sent to the temporary isolation hospital established at Stockton, north of Newcastle. Finally, in 1916-17, two small epidemics occurred, one involving the central coast area north of Sydney, where there was a scattering of cases between Sydney and Kempsey, and a more significant epidemic in the north-west of the State from Mungindi in the far north to Nevertire and Coonabarrabran further south. In 1916-17, more than 67 per cent of all smallpox cases occurred within this North Western area. In the context of small isolated country communities, the outbreak of smallpox was a traumatic and threatening event. The 66 cases of smallpox that broke out in Warren between June and December 1917, for example, must have had a devastating effect on a small community of barely 1,000 people. The North-Western outbreak was to be the last throw of the smallpox dice, as by 1917 the epidemic had run its course.

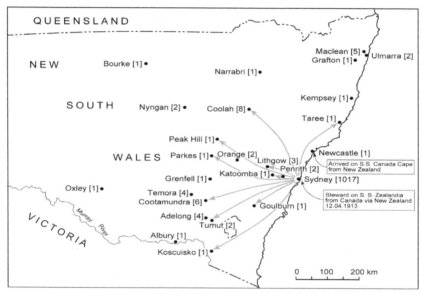

**Figure 1.3** Diffusion of Early Smallpox Cases across New South Wales, 1913.

## Smallpox in Sydney 1913-16

The impact of smallpox on the Sydney metropolitan area varied spatially. Most affected, were those living and working in the central part of Sydney, particularly the City of Sydney and adjacent suburbs. Here lived and worked most of Sydney's working and middle class. Figure 1.4 shows the morbidity rate (that is, the crude incidence rate) from smallpox by place of residence in 1913-16 to have varied from less than 1 case per thousand population, to more than 12 per thousand. Spatially, the epidemic impacted heavily on the lives of people living in central Sydney and in the inner suburbs immediately to the south of the City of Sydney. In particular, people living in the City of Sydney and the suburbs directly to the south (Redfern, Newtown, Erskinville,

Waterloo, Alexandria, St Peters and Mascot) bore the real brunt of the epidemic. In Erskinville, the incidence rate exceeded 12 cases per thousand, and in Waterloo, eight cases per thousand. In total, more than 64 percent of all cases occurred to people living in that area bounded by the City of Sydney in the north, Glebe, Newtown and St Peters in the west, Paddington and Waterloo in the east and Mascot in the south. Sydney's outer western suburbs did not escape the epidemic.

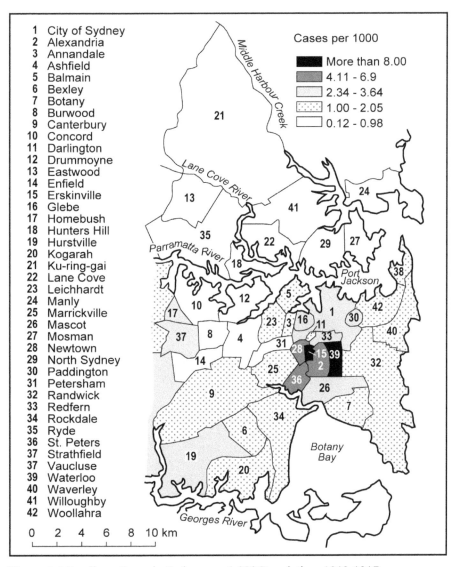

**Figure 1.4** Smallpox Cases in Sydney per 1,000 Population, 1913-1917.

Cases were also high in a belt of western suburbs extending from Parramatta, through Granville, Strathfield and Blacktown to Hurstville. As Figure 1.4 indicates, Sydney's North Shore largely escaped the ravages of the epidemic, as did a group of western suburbs extending from Petersham through Ashfield to Concord. To some extent, however, this Figure disguises one important aspect of the outbreak, which is that, particularly in the early months of the epidemic, many people were infected at their place of work, largely in central Sydney.

Overall the epidemic primarily affected young adults and adolescents, particularly males (Figure 1.5). In total, 59 percent of all cases of smallpox were males, and 72 percent of all cases during the epidemic were aged between 10 and 39 years. Almost twice as many young men as young women succumbed to the epidemic (1,056 compared to 664). The concentration of cases among young adults, particularly males, reflects the fact that the epidemic commenced among inner-city workers and from there spread to involve their families and personal contacts. It is also reflects the structure of the State's labour force in the second decade of the twentieth century, and the fact that many were infected in the workplace or adjacent streets. That many parents carried the infection to their homes is evident by the large number of young children who caught smallpox. In total, 403 children under nine years of age caught the disease. Together, adolescents, young adults and young children under nine years of age, made up 89 percent of all cases during the epidemic. The fact that the infection initially broke out in a number of city clothing factories which employed large numbers of young female employees helps explain the large numbers of young women affected.

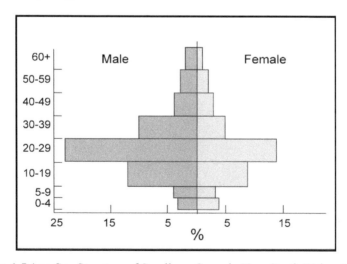

**Figure 1.5** Age-Sex Structure of Smallpox Cases in New South Wales, 1913-1917.

## The Medium of Infection

Generally, this epidemic was marked by the mildness of its symptoms, its very low infectivity rates as well as its very low mortality rate. This, and the fact that the physical symptoms of the disease were in many cases indistinguishable from the chickenpox epidemic current in Sydney at the time, undoubtedly led to a cavalier attitude among many Sydney dwellers regarding the chain of infection and normal precautions.

**Table 1.3:** Reported Source of Infection - Smallpox Cases Admitted to Quarantine Station.

|  | Number | % |
|---|---|---|
| Occupant of Same House | 298 | 54.2 |
| Next Door Neighbour | 32 | 5.8 |
| Nearby Neighbour | 16 | 2.9 |
| Working in Same Place | 50 | 9.0 |
| Attending Same School | 17 | 3.1 |
| Visited Close Relative or Friend | 88 | 15.9 |
| Other Personal Contact | 28 | 5.0 |
| Hospital Contact | 12 | 2.2 |
| Chinese Camp | 13 | 2.3 |
| Public Health Worker | 1 | 0.2 |
| **Total** | **555** | |
|  | | |

Source of Data: Cumpston and McCallum, 1925, p.68.

It is possible to identify the source of infection in 555 cases of smallpox admitted to the Quarantine Station (Table 1.3). The data in this Table highlights the importance of personal contact as the medium of infection. Direct and prolonged personal contact, either in the home, the local street, school or in the workplace, was responsible for three quarters of all smallpox cases. More transitory episodes of personal contact involving relatives or friends or other acquaintances, were responsible for an additional 21 per cent of infections. Despite this, it seems clear that many people in New South Wales remained totally ignorant of the chain of infection of the disease and the role personal contact played in its dissemination. There were many instances of people living and working in close proximity to smallpox sufferers without catching the disease. In other cases, close proximity, brought its own risks, such as that reported by the Medical Officer of Health at Newcastle, of a man suffering from smallpox whose face was covered with pustules, calmly playing cards with three neighbours, or of another case living in Gloucester who simply travelled by train to Newcastle to present himself to the Public Health authorities to discover whether or not he actually had smallpox. Another man, convinced that smallpox was not infectious, is reported kissing a severe case, only to develop smallpox himself, 14 days later. Other examples included a man sleeping in the same bed recently vacated by a smallpox patient and sharing the same handkerchief as a smallpox sufferer (see Cumpston and McCallum, 1925, p.67).

## The Official Response

### 1) Federal "Quarantine"
On July 4th 1913 the Commonwealth Government on the recommendation of the Director of Federal Quarantine Cumpston, invoked the Federal Quarantine Act and formally declared an area within 15kms of the Sydney GPO to be a "**Quarantine Area**" (Plate 1.3). Anyone living within this area who had not been successfully vaccinated against smallpox in the preceding five years was to be prohibited from journeying to another Australian State. The Commonwealth's decision to formally declare Sydney quarantined seems to have been made unilaterally without any prior warning to the New South Wales Government. As well as declaring central Sydney formally quarantined, Cumpston urged the New South Wales Government to introduce compulsory vaccination for all its citizens. These actions caused uproar throughout Sydney among politicians, businessmen and the general public, and public opinion became increasingly belligerent towards Cumpston and the Commonwealth authorities

The New South Wales Government deeply resented Commonwealth intervention; the business community feared that quarantine would severely interfere with normal business and commercial activities, while a large section of the general public remained opposed to any form of Government controls and/or compulsory vaccination. Over the course of the next four months, an acrimonious debate arose between the New South Wales and Commonwealth Governments marked by a protracted correspondence between Holman the Labour Premier of New South Wales and Joseph Cook, the Liberal Prime Minister (see Commonwealth Parliamentary Papers, 1913). This debate spilled over into the House of Representatives and the Senate, as well as the New South Wales Parliament, the Sydney Press, the medical profession and the general Sydney business community. On the 15th of September, Holman wrote to the Prime Minister asking for the Quarantine to be lifted. His letter pointed out that the epidemic was of a very mild form of smallpox, that there was very little chance of it becoming more virulent, that the danger of it spreading to other States was negligible seeing that many States had policies of compulsory vaccination, that a Vaccination Bill was soon to be put before the New South Wales Parliament and that the effects of the official Quarantine was injurious to life in New South Wales. The Prime Minister replied a few days later sympathizing with the privations Quarantine had brought to the citizens of New South Wales and pointing out that Federal intervention was to ensure that there was no chance of the disease spreading further afield. While agreeing that the disease was relatively mild, he pointed out that cases were still occurring in Sydney and that the USA experience suggested the possibility of the disease becoming more virulent. Further, he added that the numbers of people actually vaccinated against smallpox in States outside New South Wales was much lower than Holman had implied. He congratulated the New South Wales Government on preparing a Vaccination Bill for Parliament and wished that it might have been in place somewhat earlier. In brief, however, he declined to lift the Quarantine. Within a few days, Holman replied pointing out that New South Wales had no intention of passing a Bill for Compulsory Vaccination and expressed concern that the Prime Minister was not willing to lift the Quarantine. He added that he would ensure that all New South Wales Senators in the Federal Senate were apprised of the correspondence and the Commonwealth's attitude, (there was at this stage a Labour majority in the Senate). Cook replied in kind, pointing out that Quarantine would remain in place until New South Wales's provisions had been shown to be effective in preventing the spread of the disease. He went on to add, "This being so, would it not be better for you to press forward measures for the relief of the situation rather than adopt the theatrical method of endeavouring to pass the responsibility over to the Senators? Surely this latter action was entirely superfluous, as by your eagerness to give publicity to your side of the question, you had already given the correspondence to the press before its receipt by this Government. There is no room and certainly no justification for political display in these matters." (Commonwealth Parliamentary Papers, Letter Cook to Holman, 1913). The die was cast. Over the next month there were huge public meetings held in Sydney protesting the Commonwealth's actions. Finally, on the 19th of November a conference took place in Melbourne between Cumpston and the heads of the Health Departments of several of the States where the Federal Department of Quarantine's actions came under fierce attack and there was much criticism of what was seen as an unwarranted and untimely intervention by the Commonwealth (see Roe, 1984, p.123).

Ultimately, having established the principle of Federal responsibility in this area, the Commonwealth agreed to withdraw, provided that New South Wales agreed to maintain its present policy of isolating smallpox cases and contacts and agree that every person wanting to travel outside New South

Wales by land or sea, would provide a written undertaking to report any illness occurring with 21 days to the Health Department of whatever State they found themselves in at the time. A week later, the Commonwealth formally lifted Sydney's Quarantine which had been in place for over four months. Cumpston and the Commonwealth Department of Quarantine survived the incident to fight another day. From July 8th the Federal authorities decided to fumigate all mail leaving Sydney and all arriving passengers had to show evidence of successful vaccination against smallpox.

There would seem little doubt that New South Wales's trade and business suffered substantially during this period. Many overseas and interstate ships bypassed the State during this time, often discharging passengers at Newcastle or further afield, and the restrictions and interminable delays on interstate travellers imposed by the often overzealous Health authorities at the Victorian and Queensland border posts were a continued cause of complaint causing many angry scenes. There seems little doubt that inter-State trade and movement was severely affected. The mail train that left Sydney for Brisbane on July 10th carried only 19 Sydney passengers compared with the normal number of between 100 and 200. Ten days later, the steamer "Riverina" left Sydney for Melbourne with 17 passengers instead of the normal 250.

## Local Quarantine Procedures

Smallpox was officially declared to be present in Sydney by the Board of Health on the 1st of July 1913. Directions were made that smallpox cases should be conveyed to the Quarantine Station at North Head, that their homes or workplaces should be disinfected or fumigated, and that all cases and contacts should be isolated. It was also declared that vaccination should be made available free of charge to any of the public who wanted it. All smallpox cases were to be transported by motor ambulance to the Woolloomooloo wharf from where they would be transported to the Quarantine Station by steam launch. This arrangement continued until the end of March 1915 when the last case was discharged from the Quarantine Station. Smallpox cases after this date were taken to the Coast Hospital at Little Bay. Cases outside Sydney were largely treated in the isolation wards of local hospitals. In the case of the Newcastle outbreak in 1915, however, a temporary isolation hospital was established at Stockton, near the northern end of the Hunter River to which cases from the surrounding districts were removed.

The Board of Health in Sydney established a team of medical officers who were responsible for visiting every suspected case. Their task was made more difficult by virtue of the fact that Sydney was also experiencing an epidemic of chickenpox in 1913. If the medical officer confirmed the case as smallpox, the person was removed to quarantine and all contacts offered vaccination. Initially, all contacts were also transported to the Quarantine Station, some forcibly, and detained until vaccination proved successful. Later in the epidemic, however, the sheer numbers involved made this policy impossible and only those who refused vaccination were removed to North Head. Later in the epidemic, when the numbers of cases and contacts had declined somewhat, the original process of removing both cases and contacts to the Quarantine Station was revived.

Between July 1913 and March 1915, 2,425 people were sent to the Quarantine Station at North Head, 1,557 as smallpox cases and 868 as contacts (Plates 1.4 and 1.5). Figure 1.6 illustrates the temporal flow of admissions to the Quarantine Station in the July 1913 –March 1915 period. In the case of persons suffering from smallpox, there were two major periods of removal. The first corresponded with the official announcement of the epidemic and the months immediately following, when 967 people were quarantined. The second, from May until November 1914, saw another 459 admissions. The pattern of quarantining contacts was slightly more variable with peaks in July 1913, from November 1913 until March 1914 and from May to July in 1914. Most cases sent to North Head were released back into the community after they were deemed to no longer be infectious. Usually this was after about 14 days. The pattern of discharges from the Quarantine Station are shown in Figure 1.7 The largest number of people (cases and contacts) to be held at the Quarantine Station at any one time during the epidemic was 309, and this occurred early in the epidemic (Figure 1.6).

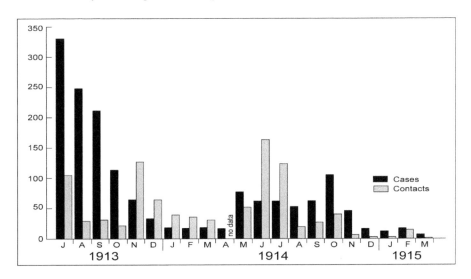

**Figure 1.6** Smallpox Cases and Contacts Sent to Quarantine Station, 1913-1915.

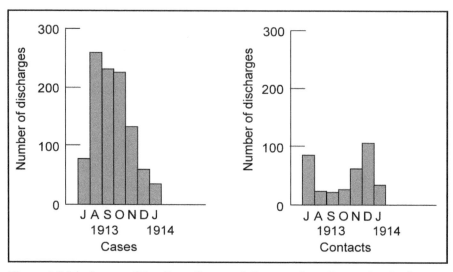

**Figure 1.7** Discharges of Smallpox Cases and Contacts from Quarantine Station, 1913-1914.

## Vaccination

After 1853 all the Australian colonies other than New South Wales and Queensland, passed acts or ordinances requiring the compulsory vaccination of all children against smallpox. Only in Victoria and South Australia, however, was such legislation pursued with any vigour and even in these Colonies, people expressed considerable misgivings over such government rules and regulations. Despite a number of attempts, no such legislation was ever enacted in New South Wales. At the height of the 1881-82 smallpox epidemic, attempts were made to introduce a Compulsory Vaccination Bill, but they foundered in the face of a concentrated campaign conducted by a strong opposition (see Curson, 1985). Figure 1.8 displays the ebb and flow of vaccinations against smallpox in the Australian Colonies/States between 1850 and 1915. In the case of New South Wales, the rise and fall of vaccinations represents a barometer of public fears and anxiety, and the perception of personal threat from particular epidemic outbreaks both local and in other parts of Australia. Hence, there were small peaks in vaccinations in 1869 (Melbourne epidemic), in 1872 (Bendigo epidemic), in 1877, 1881-82 (Sydney epidemics), 1903 (Launceston epidemic) and in 1913 (Sydney epidemic).

Four days after the 1913 epidemic was officially proclaimed, the New South Wales Board of Health passed a resolution calling on the New South Wales Government to immediately pass a Compulsory Vaccination Bill, and a draft Bill was forwarded to the Premier. A day later, Cumpston added his voice to such a request. Over the next few months the New South Wales medical fraternity and public health officials would maintain a flow of information, articles and letters stating the benefits of compulsory vaccination against smallpox. Like during the 1881-82 smallpox epidemic, anti and pro-vaccination camps girded for action (see Curson, 1985). Both camps bombarded the Sydney newspapers with letters and articles. On July 10th a deputation representing the British Medical Association, the Chambers of Manufacturers and Commerce plus various shipping interests, waited on the Premier to urge the passage of a compulsory vaccination bill. A week later, the Premier announced that Cabinet would proceed with such a bill during the next sitting of Parliament. A day later, the Premier added that his intention was for the bill to simply apply to Sydney's "infantile population".

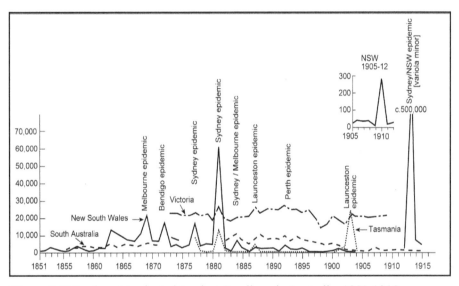

**Figure 1.8** Numbers Vaccinated Against Smallpox in Australia, 1851-1915.

On July 21st the anti-vaccination camp launched a major public campaign to oppose a Vaccination Bill. Huge public meetings were held over the next three days during which Parliamentarians, businessmen and other professionals argued vehemently against the benefits of vaccination. This was a re-run of 1881-82 all over again. The arguments were familiar. On July 21st to the hundreds who packed into Kings-Hall in Sydney, Dr W. Adams, a doctor of laws, moving the motion again compulsory vaccination, strongly argued that the protection offered by vaccination was a "grotesque superstition" and that there was not a shred of evidence in favour of vaccination. Quoting Dr Alfred Russell Wallace, who he described as the "greatest scientist of the day", he stated that vaccination "was an illusion and a gigantic imposture." His audience applauded heartily. He further claimed that 50,000 deaths from vaccination

23

had occurred in the United Kingdom annually. He then commented broadly on the medical profession's support for compulsory vaccination in New South Wales, claiming that out of about 1,800 practitioners, only 200 were actually entitled to call themselves "Doctor". The other 1,600 were simply, bachelors of medicine. W.J. Spencer, seconding the motion, claimed that New South Wales had always been free from the curse of compulsory vaccination and "that anyone submitting to be cow-poxed would submit to anything."(Laughter and cheers from the audience). With increasing vehemence, he declared that people in New South Wales were being shepherded through Vaccination depots like so many sheep"(*Daily Telegraph*, July 22, 1913, p.8). The motion was carried with acclaim and a delegation formed to meet the Premier. The following day the debate was taken up in the New South Wales Legislative Council where James Wilson, MLC argued that "gallons of lymph was being poured into people by men not qualified."(*Daily Telegraph*, July 23, 1913, p.10). The debate continued, in the press, in Parliament and at public meetings. The same day, the New South Wales Labor Council passed a motion strongly protesting against the proposed legislation making vaccination compulsory.

On July 25th the anti-vaccinationists called another public meeting in Sydney's Protestant Hall. Hundreds attended, and in an emotional meeting, heard of the dangers of vaccination and the fact that the medical community was divided on its benefits. Speaking again, James Wilson MLC likened the scenes at the Town Hall Vaccination Depot to "the branding of sheep, which rushed afterwards to the pastures, where they were free till they were wanted again for their wool or their meat."(*Daily Telegraph*, July 26, 1913. p.13). A week later at a third public meeting of several hundred people, it was claimed that every death from heart failure that had taken place during the epidemic, could be ascribed to the consequences of vaccination (*Daily Telegraph*, Aug. 1, 1913, p.10). On the other side, the Sydney newspapers were full of articles and letters from medical men and others defending the efficacy of vaccination. The outcome was that the Premier and Cabinet, under threat from a Censure motion in Parliament and concerned by the wave of anti-vaccination sentiment sweeping Sydney, delayed presenting the bill to Parliament. When the Bill was actually presented to Parliament for its first reading on September 16th, smallpox cases were still occurring in Sydney but Holman faced a divided Caucus, an antagonistic Labor Council and Health Committee of the City Council, and the opposition of many influential businessmen and city leaders. Confronted by such a dilemma he took the only way out and presented the Bill to Parliament as a Non-Party Bill. The second reading took place in early October and the third reading, two weeks later. At the third reading, the Bill was defeated after a bitter debate, and New South Wales consequently maintained its reputation as a bastion against compulsory vaccination.

# The Smallpox Epidemic of 1913-1917

Regardless of the broader Vaccination debate, as soon as the disease was officially recognized in New South Wales, measures were put in place for the vaccination of all hospital staff, public officials and any of the general public who requested it. Anticipating a large public demand, the Government moved to establish a lymph farm in the grounds of the Coast Hospital. Initially, lymph for vaccination purposes was obtained from the Commonwealth Quarantine Department, but after a few weeks it was found to not give very good results and in some cases, to produce severe side-effects. Lymph was then obtained from New Zealand as well as from the Government farm. Free public vaccination depots opened their doors in Sydney on July 3rd, and during the next six months approximately 500,000 persons sought vaccination, including approximately 231,000 in the Sydney Metropolitan Area. Vaccination Depots were also established in country areas which had to rely on private practitioners to carry out vaccinations (Table 1.4). As Figure 1.9 suggests, once the public became aware of the smallpox threat in early July there was an immediate rush for vaccination. In Sydney, vaccinations reached a peak between the 8th and 12th of July in 1913 (Figure 1.9 and Table 1.4). On these five days, almost 56,000 Sydneysiders were vaccinated. Such was the demand, that new vaccination depots had to be established at various suburban locations throughout the city, including, at Redfern, Newtown, North Sydney, Parramatta, Mascot, Balmain and Glebe. By the second week after the epidemic had been officially declared, a total of 63,671 people had sought vaccination. Roughly 53 percent of all Sydney vaccinations took place in the first three weeks of the epidemic, after which the level of vaccination fell away. Largely vaccinations followed the ebb and flow of the epidemic. As the number of cases declared fell away, so too did the clamour for vaccination, only to relight again following the discovery of a cluster of new cases.

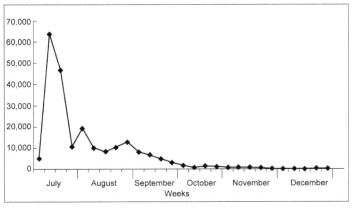

**Figure 1.9** Smallpox Vaccinations in Sydney, 1913.

| Table 1.4: Numbers Vaccinated Against Smallpox in NSW 1913 –1917 | | |
|---|---|---|
| **Year** | **Number** | **Comments** |
| 1913 | 500,000 | Approximately 231,000 in Sydney |
| 1914 | 6,628 | Does not include vaccinations by private practitioners |
| 1915 | 10,159 | Most were inmates of institutions |
| 1916 | 2,618 | Does not include considerable numbers vaccinated by private practitioners in Newcastle area |
| 1917 | 4,663 | |
| | | |
| Source: Reports, Director-General of Public Health, NSW, 1913-18. | | |

## Public Reaction

There seems little doubt that early on in the epidemic public anxiety and fear was fanned by the newspaper headlines and accounts of the outbreak, including reports of the Federal Quarantine, the need to vaccinate, and the regular daily tally sheets and personal stories of the epidemic's victims. To this, must be added the behaviour of most City employers in insisting that all their staff be vaccinated or leave work, plus the Government's decision to vaccinate all schoolchildren in infected areas. Indeed, such was the pressure that employers placed on their employees to be vaccinated, that the New South Wales Labor Council was deluged with complaints of victimization, of employees being told, "Get vaccinated, or don't come back to work." All this, and the reports of the stampede of people to get vaccinated during the early months of the epidemic, undoubtedly helped create a climate of fear and apprehension. In all of this, the newspapers of the day played an important part. On July 3rd the Sydney newspapers ran large headlines, **"VACCINATE, VACCINATE,"** as well as articles on *"The Causes of Smallpox – the Most Contagious of Diseases."* On July 5th Sydney people were greeted with the banner headline, "QUARANTINED ... **SYDNEY UNDER HEALTH LAW** ... DECLARED INFECTED," and two days later by the headline, "VIGILANT! **FIGHTING SMALLPOX.**"

The rush to get vaccinated against smallpox in the period prior to the end of July created extraordinary scenes of panic and hysteria in inner Sydney, such as the huge crowd of many thousands that besieged the Town Hall Vaccination Depot on July 7th. People battled and elbowed each other in a mad frenzy to get through the doors, and the crowd, in the words of the *Daily Telegraph*, was "representative of every class of the community. Six motor cars drawn up outside the town-hall were waiting for ladies, dressed in the height of fashion, hats with big ostrich feathers and all, who were struggling to get nearer the front … There was the city businessman who "thought he might as well get it done, as it costs nothing." He was violently pushed aside by the factory girl who had been tuned to impulsiveness by the arbitrary dictum of the manager. "Get vaccinated or get the sack." (*Daily Telegraph*, July 9, 1913, p 9.). Over the next few days hundreds of men, woman and children fought to get into the Town Hall and great scenes of confusion and anxiety were everywhere. The establishment of suburban vaccination depots helped ease the crush, but scenes of panic continued for a number of weeks. By the 21st of July, more than 121,000 people had sought vaccination in Sydney. Towards the end of 1913, when it was becoming clear that the outbreak of smallpox was very mild, that infection did not mean an untimely and unsightly death, and that the chances of catching smallpox, even off an infected person, was very low, most of the general public lost interest, and a plague of indifference replaced the earlier anxiety and fear, only to be momentarily upset when smallpox resurfaced the following year.

On July 11 the Archbishop Kelly undoubtedly added to public disquiet, by instructing the clergy that the collect **Por tempore pestilentiae** should be recited for nine days. Apart from the panic to be vaccinated and the initial fear of infection, the area which produced the most public apprehension and hostility concerned what became known as **The Border Blockade**. Primarily this took place at the New South Wales-Victorian border at Albury, where the Victorian health authorities maintained a strict and rigorous surveillance. When passengers arrived aboard the Sydney-Melbourne express at Wodonga, the Victorian officials checked all vaccination certificates. Any passenger without evidence of successful vaccination, or for whom there was any doubt, was refused entry to Victoria and off-loaded. Regularly this produced angry scenes of confrontation, such as occurred on July 14th when 50 passengers were told to disembark, having been refused permission to cross the border. Some had to be forcibly removed from the train, and all had to return to Albury, some in a railway mail van, others by cab. This was a pattern that was to replay itself out virtually every day the Sydney-Melbourne train arrived, and eventually Wodonga residents bitterly complained about having "infected" passengers dumped on them.

## Conclusions

In the case of the 1913-17 smallpox epidemic in New South Wales, it seems reasonably clear that the official method adopted for control and containment such as identification, notification, isolation, disinfection, vaccination and supervision of contacts, was a competent and successful way to control the disease in spite of the failure to secure compulsory vaccination. Had the disease been the more virulent form of smallpox, however, then things might have been very different. Generally, the very mild nature of the infection and the almost absence of deaths, meant that after an initial wave of fear and panic, the public largely came to see the disease as a necessary evil, and by the end of 1913, smallpox had almost come to be accepted like many childhood diseases.

## CHAPTER 2

# The Mysterious Disease: Australian "X" Disease 1917-18

In early 1917, an acute, severe and highly lethal illness, largely affecting young children, was reported throughout parts of New South Wales. The illness was marked by an abrupt onset, with headaches, convulsions, rigidity with varying degrees of paralysis, mental confusion, coma, occasionally respiratory paralysis and for many sufferers, death within a few days. The high mortality, severity of symptoms and rapid progress of the disease excited considerable comment and stunned local officials and medical authorities alike. Nothing quite like it had been seen before, even though outbreaks of meningitis and poliomyelitis were becoming more common. Many thought they were dealing with a particularly acute form of poliomyelitis.

In March 1917 public attention was drawn to a particular outbreak of this disease in Broken Hill in the far west of New South Wales, where within a few weeks, 14 people had fallen ill, 12 dying within 3-5 days. Within days of its appearance, the Sydney newspapers were talking about the "New Mysterious Disease" and later the medical fraternity dubbed it "X" Disease (See *Sydney Morning Herald*, 27 March, 1917, p.8; Cleland et.al. 1918, pp.150-280 and Cleland, 1924, pp.87-88) (Plate 2.1.) In the Broken Hill cases, the disease was marked by its sudden onset and rapid progress. Most patients reported a headache, followed by general malaise and drowsiness, confusion, irritability and weakness particularly in the limbs. After a day or so, most patients lapsed into semi-unconsciousness. Eventually, the sufferers slipped into a state of delirium followed by respiratory failure and death. The severity of the illness and the high mortality rate raised considerable concern. Reporting on the Broken Hill outbreak, Burnell, a House Surgeon at the Broken Hill Hospital, commented "… we have a symptom-complex which does not conform to any of the ordinary diseases, and I am hoping that other cases may be recorded which will lead to an advance in the study of aetiology and treatment." (Burnell, 1917, pp.157-159). His wish was to be granted, for in the following year there were 25 more cases and 23 deaths from the disease in the Broken Hill area, as well as more cases throughout New South Wales, Queensland and Victoria. Burnell's desire to unravel the disease's aetiology, however, was to remain frustrated, for it would be another 34 years before the true nature of the disease would be finally revealed. Although only 70 cases of this new disease were formally reported in New South Wales during 1917, and 58 the following year, there were undoubtedly more, as many mild cases would have gone unnoticed or unreported (Table 2.1). This was certainly true of a number of cases in and around the small towns of Bourke and Walgett and it was probably true of other parts of the state as well.

**Table 2.1:** Cases and Deaths Australian "X" Disease, 1917-25

|  | 1917 | | 1918 | | 1922 | | 1925 | |
|---|---|---|---|---|---|---|---|---|
|  | Cases | Deaths | Cases | Deaths | Cases | Deaths | Cases | Deaths |
| Queensland | 44 | 22 | 5 | 2 | 75 | 49 | 11 | 10 |
| NSW | 70* | 39 | 58 | 46 |  |  | 10 | 6 |
| Victoria |  |  | 13 |  |  |  |  |  |
| Sth Australia |  |  | 1 |  |  |  |  |  |
| Total | 114* | 61 | 77 | 48 | 75 | 49 | 21 | 16 |

*Not including a number of cases at Walgett and Bourke.

Source: Cleland et al., 1918.

## Clinical Signs and Symptoms

The clinical features of the new disease were first described by Burnell in 1917, drawing upon his personal experience of the Broken Hill outbreak (Burnell, 1917, pp.157-159; Burnell, 1918, pp.278-280). Breinl provided more information the following year, based on his experience of Queensland cases

(Breinl, 1917, p.454; Breinl, 1918, p.209), and Campbell in his section of the official New South Wales report on the epidemic provided the most detailed summary of the clinical manifestations of the disease (Campbell in Cleland, et.al, 1919). All drew attention to the sudden onset of headache and in some cases, vomiting, commonly followed by convulsions and fever. This was rapidly followed in many cases, by a general lassitude accompanied by mental confusion, irritability, muscular pains and lack of coordination, particularly in the neck and limbs. In the words of Campbell, "…it was not surprising that some men who staggered into hospital suffering from the disease were thought to be intoxicated or suffering from heatstroke" (Campbell in Cleland, et. al, 1919, p.154). Others were thought to be insane, such as George Box, a miner from Broken Hill who fell ill in February 1918 and was initially declared insane before being confirmed as ill and transferred to hospital. From this point the disease progressed very rapidly to a stage of fever, convulsions, mental confusion, neck stiffness and limb rigidity. Campbell described the way some patients thrashed about on their beds, waving their arms and legs, while others rolled their head from side to side, suffered considerable muscle tremors, ground their teeth together and regularly closed their eyes. In many cases, coma and death followed within hours (Campbell in Cleland, et.al, 1919, p.154).

## What Disease was it and how did it spread?

Early medical practitioners such as Litchfield and Breinl believed they were confronted by a form of severe meningitis, but tests and post mortems did not confirm their diagnosis (See Litchfield, 1917; Breinl, 1917). Noting changes in the brain and spinal cord of sufferers, Breinl finally concluded that what he was encountering was an acute form of poliomyelitis (Breinl, 1918, p.229). He also succeeded in producing a fatal case in a laboratory monkey by inoculating it with material taken from the cerebrospinal fluid of a fatal case. Burnell, who provided the first detailed report of cases in Broken Hill, believed that he had isolated a specific bacterium, but later attempts to confirm this proved unsuccessful. Mathewson and Latham, reporting on 17 similar cases in The Children's Hospital in Brisbane, largely agreed with Breinl that the disease was an acute form of poliomyelitis (Mathewson and Latham, 1917, pp.352-353). Campbell, in reviewing the clinical evidence of previous studies and the New South Wales cases in 1917-18, concluded that what they were confronted with, was a unique disease and that the case for it being an acute form of poliomyelitis, remained unproved (Campbell in Cleland et.al, 1919, pp.154-158). In particular, he was swayed by the fact that unlike poliomyelitis, the present disease was characterised by a preponderance of meningitic cases, by a very high mortality rate, by a number of adult cases as well as young children, and by few paralytic outcomes. Finally, he questioned if this was an outbreak of poliomyelitis, why was it confined to specific New South Wales country areas without any cases occurring in metropolitan areas? The medical authorities were clearly in something of a quandary. Where the disease had originated and how it spread from one person to another also occupied the minds of the New South Wales medical authorities.

The official report on the epidemic, explored a variety of possibilities of transmission and endemicity, including animal reservoirs and a variety of invertebrate vectors, including flies, fleas, bed bugs, mosquitoes and fowl ticks (Cleland, Campbell and Bradley, 1919). Fowl ticks, in particular attracted some attention but attempts to transmit the disease from ticks to monkeys were unsuccessful. Numerous efforts were made to inoculate a variety of laboratory animals with the material taken from human cases. The virus was successfully transmitted to monkeys, sheep, a horse and a calf. Other experiments with smaller animals, including guinea-pigs, dogs and kittens proved inconclusive. In cases where the disease developed in such animals, the signs and symptoms were indistinguishable from human cases. Finally, the report concluded that none of the invertebrates considered could be held responsible for the outbreak or its transmission. When it came to explaining the disease's diffusion in time and space, Cleland and his team were equally perplexed. Having dismissed the possibility of an animal reservoir/host or vector of the disease, they had difficulty in explaining the spatial association between new and older cases, and the fact that cases of the disease appeared simultaneously in widely scattered and separated geographic parts of the state. Noticing that many cases appeared, "almost contemporaneously, in towns along the North-Western and Western system of railways", they concluded that the disease was probably spread from one area to another by human "carriers" who in most cases must have passed through Sydney (the hub of the state's railway system).

The possibility of mosquitoes being involved as the vector of the disease does not seem to have occurred to medical authorities in 1917-18 or for that matter for the next 20 or 30 years. What people failed to appreciate in 1917-18, was that most cases of "X" Disease occurred in close proximity to an inland waterways system, such as along the Darling River in the west, the Barwon, Gwydir and Namoi in the north, the Macquarie near Dubbo, and the Murrumbidgee in the south. This fact, and the prevailing La Nina conditions which led to widespread summer rains and flooding and a proliferation of mosquito and water bird populations during the early summers of 1917 and 1918, seems to have gone largely unnoticed in accounts of the epidemic.

## Temporal Distribution

Figure 2.1 illustrates the monthly distribution of cases in the 1917 and 1918 outbreaks. Both distributions show a typical "epidemic curve". The 1917 epidemic probably began in late 1916 in a mild form and really only came to public notice early in 1917. The first case, a two year-old female is recorded as taking place on the 3rd of October 1916 at Boggabri. No new cases were recorded until late January 1917. By February, it was apparent that something unusual was happening. Cases continued to be reported and the epidemic reached a peak in March –April, and then disappeared almost as quickly as it had appeared some months earlier. By comparison, in 1918 the epidemic peaked a month earlier in February, and then gradually declined over the ensuing two months. Deaths largely followed the same temporal distribution, with peaks in March (1917) and February (1918). In 1917, most deaths occurred in a two week period between 11th and 29th of March. In 1918, from the 4th of February until the end of the month, hardly a day went by without a death from "X" Disease being recorded somewhere in the state.

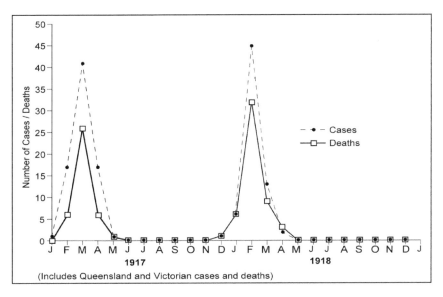

**Figure 2.1** Monthly Distribution of Cases and Deaths from Australian "X" Disease, 1917-1918.

## Who Was Affected?

One interesting aspect of the epidemic was that it primarily attacked young children, particularly males. Figure 2.2 illustrates the age-sex distribution of 125 cases for which age-sex data were available in 1917-18. The predominance of young children under the age of 10 years is immediately evident. Just over 61 percent of all cases were aged under 10, with 37 percent being aged less than 5 years. More than 72 percent of all cases were children aged under 15 years of age. We now know that this was probably because after repeated exposure to the virus, many adults develop a level of immunity, so that severe cases of the disease are relatively rare. Young children, by comparison, do not seem to share this immunity, and first exposure to the virus, may be the most dangerous. Newborn babies, by contrast may inherit a degree of immunity from their mother. Males also contributed the majority of cases making up 72.5 percent of all cases including 65 percent of those aged under 5 years and 66 percent of the under 15 year age group. Apart from young children, males aged over 30 also played their part in the epidemic contributing 19 percent of all cases, including 11.5 percent to those aged between 30 and 49 years.

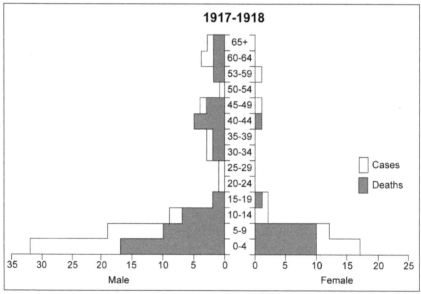

**Figure 2.2** Age-Sex Structure of Cases and Deaths from Australian "X" Disease, 1917-1918.

## Mortality

The epidemic was noted for its virulence and high mortality rate. This was particularly the case during the 1918 outbreak when the mortality rate was close to 80 percent. By comparison, in 1917 just over 53 percent of those who caught the disease died. For the two years combined, the mortality rate was 65 percent. Overall, 54 of the 91 children under 15 years of age who had the misfortune to catch the disease in 1917-18 died, a mortality rate of

59 percent (Tables 2.2 and 2.3). In 1918, child mortality was much higher, with 31 deaths out of 41 cases, a mortality rate of 76 percent. For very young children aged under four years the mortality rate was more than 77 percent in 1918 compared to only 37 per cent in 1917. Although the epidemic impacted heaviest on young children, adults were not spared its effects. Of the 10 people aged between 30 and 59 years, who caught the disease in 1918, nine died. Again, the 1917 epidemic was slightly gentler on adults, with only six of the 11 adults aged between 30-59 dying.

**Table 2.2:** Mortality by Age and Sex NSW

| | 1917 | | | | 1918 | | | | 1917-1918 | | | |
|---|---|---|---|---|---|---|---|---|---|---|---|---|
| | Cases | | Deaths | | Cases | | Deaths | | Cases | | Deaths | |
| Age Groups | M | F | M | F | M | F | M | F | M | F | M | F |
| 0-4 | 15 | 12 | 4 | 6 | 17 | 5 | 13 | 4 | 32 | 17 | 17 | 10 |
| 5-14 | 15 | 8 | 8 | 5 | 13 | 6 | 9 | 5 | 28 | 14 | 17 | 10 |
| 15-29 | 1 | 1 | 0 | 1 | 3 | 1 | 2 | 1 | 4 | 2 | 2 | 1 |
| 30-59 | 10 | 1 | 6 | 0 | 8 | 2 | 8 | 1 | 18 | 3 | 14 | 1 |
| 60+ | 5 | 0 | 2 | 0 | 2 | 0 | 2 | 0 | 7 | 0 | 4 | 0 |
| Total | 46 | 22 | 27 | 12 | 44 | 14 | 36 | 10 | 95 | 36 | 63 | 22 |

Source: Cleland, et.al, 1919.

**Table 2.3:** Mortality Rates by Age and Sex Deaths as % of Cases, NSW

| | 1917 | | | 1918 | | | 1917-1918 | | |
|---|---|---|---|---|---|---|---|---|---|
| Age Groups | M | F | Total | M | F | Total | M | F | Total |
| 0-4 | 26.7 | 50.0 | 37.3 | 76.5 | 80.0 | 77.3 | 53.1 | 58.8 | 55.1 |
| 5-14 | 53.3 | 62.5 | 56.5 | 69.2 | 83.3 | 73.4 | 50.0 | 58.8 | 53.3 |
| 15-29 | 0.0 | 100 | 50.0 | 66.6 | 0.0 | 50.0 | 50.0 | 50.0 | 50.0 |
| 30-59 | 60.0 | 0.0 | 54.5 | 100 | 50 | 90.0 | 77.8 | 33.3 | 71.4 |
| 60+ | 40.0 | 0.0 | 40.0 | 100 | 0 | 100 | 57.1 | 0.0 | 57.1 |
| Total | 52.9 | 54.5 | 53.4 | 81.8 | 71.4 | 79.3 | 66.3 | 61.1 | 65.0 |

Source: Data from Cleland, et.al, 1919.

## Geographical distribution

In 1917 the epidemic was very largely concentrated in the far north of the state along the Macintyre River between Gooniwindi and Mungindi and along the nearby river systems of the Gwydir and Namoi (Figure 2.3). Apart from this, there were a cluster of cases in Broken Hill and surrounding areas, at Menindee, along the Darling River as well as a couple of cases at Nyngan and Warren. By contrast, the 1918 outbreak was more spatially diffused, with a cluster of cases along the Murrumbidgee River in the south of the state, between Currathool and Narrandera, a cluster of cases at Broken Hill, as well as cases near the Macquarie river system between Nyngan and Dubbo, extending northwards to Coonamble. There were also a number of cases along the Namoi River between Wee Waa and Boggabri. The 1918 outbreak also seems to have extended across the New South Wales/Victoria border south of Tocumwal, with at least 13 cases along the Goulburn River Valley, including at least six deaths (Figure 2.4).

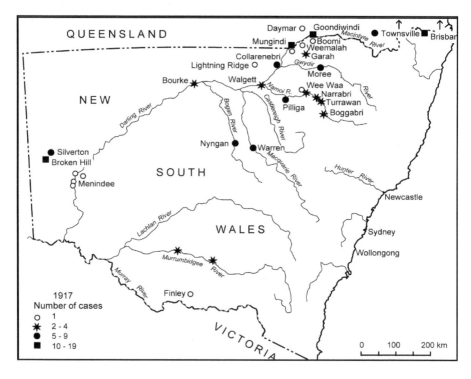

**Figure 2.3** Geographical Distribution of Australian "X" Disease Cases, 1917

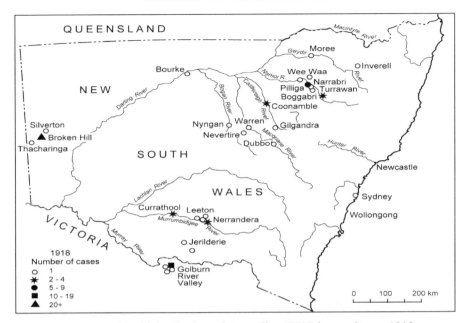

**Figure 2.4** Geographical Distribution of Australian "X" Disease Cases, 1918.

## Diffusion in Space

Despite the fact that official attention was first drawn to the Broken Hill outbreak in late February early March, it would seem clear that the 1917 epidemic had begun somewhat earlier. Reconstruction of the cases in New South Wales suggests that the epidemic first commenced in the Gooniwindi area of Queensland near the border with New South Wales in January or February or possibly earlier, and from there, extended across the border into New South Wales and along the Barwon River in the vicinity of Mungindi. From here, the disease spread south to involve Walgett via Collarenabri. A scatter of cases also occurred along the Namoi River between Walgett and Boggabri. Some weeks later, the first case occurred in Broken Hill, as well as a case to the southeast in Menindee. Over the next month, cases of the disease began appearing in a number of country towns throughout the state. In March the disease reached its peak and then subsequently declined so that by May it had disappeared.[1]

In the following year, the disease first appeared almost simultaneously in four widely scattered locations in January, at Broken Hill, in the south along the Murrumbidgee River, in the central part of the state between Nyngan, Dubbo and Gilgandera, and along the Namoi River in the north, at Narrabri.

---

[1] A case was recorded in Nyngan in December 1917, but was probably a forerunner of the 1918 outbreak.

Subsequent cases followed in the same areas over the next three months (see Figures 2.3 and 2.4). In 1918, the disease appeared almost simultaneously in January in a number of different parts of the state, at Narrabri, in the Gilgandra-Nyngan area at Broken Hill and along the Murrumbidgee River between Carrathool and Narrandera. Subsequently, more cases occurred in these areas over the ensuing three months.

## The Disease Revealed

Outbreaks of a disease resembling "X" Disease occurred in New South Wales and Queensland in 1922 and 1925, after which the disease seems to have disappeared until 1951. In 1922 it is possible that a major epidemic of "X" Disease occurred in Queensland, principally in the Brisbane and Ipswich areas. The Annual Report of the Queensland Commissioner of Public Health records 75 cases of what was described as "Epidemic Polio Encephalitis" with 49 deaths (Queensland Government, 1922, p.11). All cases were children under 14 years of age and largely the epidemic involved the area between Roma, Ipswich and Brisbane with a few cases at Rockhampton. A further 11 cases and 10 deaths were recorded in Queensland in 1925, mainly in the Townsville area. In the same year, 10 cases also occurred in Broken Hill, with six deaths. After this, the disease seems to have slipped from official records until an outbreak of a similar form of encephalitis occurred in the Murray Valley during the late summer of 1950-51. The disease was given the name Murray Valley encephalitis (MVE) and clinical and histo-pathological studies indicated a severe viral encephalitis with features virtually identical to that of "X" Disease in 1917-18 (See Miles, 1951, p.799; and French, 1952, pp.100-103). Experiments carried out by McLean revealed the role played by mosquitoes as the disease vector (McLean, 1953, p.481), and later serological studies of human, animal and water-bird populations by Anderson (Anderson, et.al, 1953, p.447) indicated that a high proportion of human and water-bird populations carried antibodies to the virus. This and other work established the role played by water-birds and mosquitoes in maintaining the virus in natural disease cycles.

Further evidence of what the 1917-18 disease was, also came in the early 1950s, when McLean and Stevens examined blood samples from 92 people who had been resident in Broken Hill during the 1917-18 epidemic of "X Disease" (McLean and Stevenson, 1954, p.636). In 19 cases, neutralizing antibody to Murray Valley encephalitis was found in their blood and only two of the 69 who could not have been exposed to "X Disease" returned a positive result (McLean and Stevenson, 1954). This, and other evidence, strongly suggests that if "X Disease" was not actually Murray Valley encephalitis, then it was caused by a virus antigenically very similar to Murray Valley encephalitis.

It now seems clear that the virus is probably endemic to much of Northern Australia; with disease foci in Northern Western Australia and possibly the Northern Territory and Northern Queensland, and that the main vector of the disease is the mosquito Culex annulirostris. It would also seem that the disease is maintained in permanent water-bird-mosquito cycles with water-birds acting as the vertebrate host, although it is possible that other vertebrates may also be involved. The actual factors responsible for the long-term survival of the virus in endemic reservoirs and the establishment of epizootic and epidemic foci, however, remain elusive. It is possible that this disease has caused cases in humans throughout most of Australia's history and that many cases escaped recognition because of its mildness. Long-term and frequent exposure to the virus may have also bred a degree of immunity in sectors of the population, particularly among Aboriginal communities as well as European settlers.

## Environmental Markers in 1916-18

Historically, outbreaks of Murray Valley encephalitis have all occurred during summer or late autumn, and would seem to be related to extended periods of above average spring and early summer rainfall in northern and eastern Australia, filling the catchments of the Darling-Murray River system. Such conditions would seem conducive to a build up of mosquito numbers and an increase in water-bird populations (see Miles and Howes, 1953). Southern Oscillation Index (SOI) data suggests that after a strong El Nino period between 1913 and early 1916, Australia entered a very strong La Nina phase from mid 1916 which was to last until early 1918 (Australian Bureau of Meteorology). Figure 2.5 plots the SOI for the period January 1916 until April 1918, as well as cases of "X" Disease that occurred in 1917 and 1918. From mid-late 1916 until March/April of 1917, well above average rainfall and local flooding in north and parts of eastern Australia, would have greatly enhanced the breeding cycle and distribution of both water birds and mosquito populations (Forbes, 1978, p.7).

It now seems clear that rainfall in northern and eastern Australia was substantially higher than normal in the spring and early summer of 1917 and 1918 (Forbes, 1978, p.7). Figure 2.6 plots rainfall data for the Lower Carpentaria district for the period July 1916 to May 1918. It is clear from this data that rainfall in the October/November – February/March periods of 1916-17 and 1917-18 was well above the average (Miles and Howes, 1953). The same was true of rainfall in the Darling River catchment and at Broken Hill (Figure 2.7). In 1917, cases of "X" Disease peaked in March 1917 after nine months of La Nina conditions. In 1918, "X" Disease cases peaked a month earlier in February, following a very pronounced La Nina period from early in the year. It would seem clear, with the benefit of hindsight, that conditions in January-February 1917 and 1918 were ideal for the outbreak of a mosquito-borne disease. Hot summer temperatures following a lengthy period of above average spring and early summer rainfall with widespread local flooding.

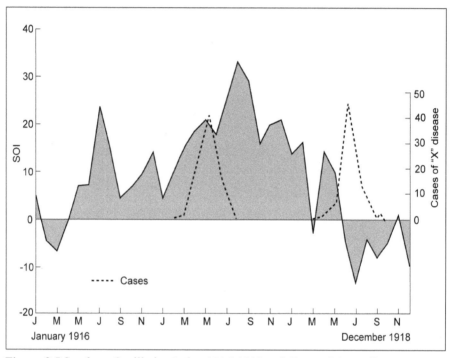

**Figure 2.5** Southern Oscillation Index 1916-1918 and Cases of Australian "X" Disease.

## Conclusion

The appearance of "X" disease in 1917 was a turning point in Australia's epidemiological history. While the disease had probably circulated amongst its natural host – water birds, for centuries, this was the first recorded outbreak of what was to become known as Murray Valley encephalitis. In 1917-18 the disease stunned the medical community with its virulence and high mortality, particularly among young children. The outbreaks of "X" disease all occurred in late summer-early autumn in the hot dry areas of New South Wales and Southern Queensland and were undoubtedly related to the prevailing La Nina conditions and the preceding months of heavy rainfall. It was not until more than 30 years later, however, that the disease was conclusively identified and the role of water birds and mosquitoes fully appreciated.

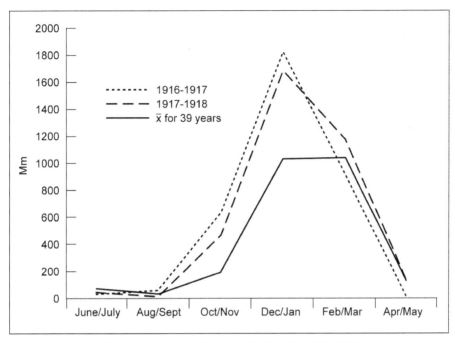

**Figure 2.6**: Rainfall Patterns Lower Carpentaria District, 1916-1977.

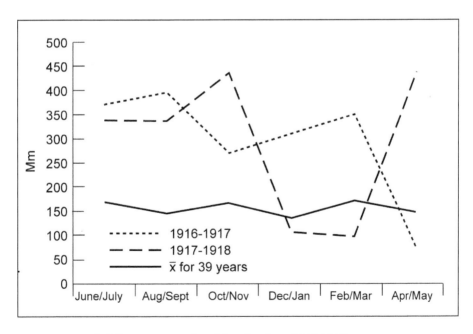

**Figure 2.7**: Rainfall Patterns Darling River Region, 1916-1917

# CHAPTER 3

# Beware the Flu! New South Wales and the Influenza Pandemic of 1919

Six months before the end of the First World War a new and deadly form of influenza emerged and swept across the world. Popularly referred to as 'Spanish Flu' the disease probably affected between 25 and 35 percent of the world's population and killed more than 40 million over the next 12 months. As pandemics stand, the 1918-19 influenza outbreak was without doubt the deadliest and most destructive in recorded human history. In a handful of months it spread around the world impacting upon virtually every aspect of life, disrupting normal social and economic activities, and affecting communities with a virulence not seen before or since. Australia managed to avoid the infection raging elsewhere in the world until early 1919. By the latter part of 1919, however, at least 15,000 Australians had died from influenza and possibly 1.5 million had caught the disease. In New South Wales more than 500,000 had the misfortune to catch influenza during 1919 and 6,244 died from the disease. In the Sydney metropolitan area, roughly 37 percent of the population or 340,000 people had influenza in 1919 and more than 4,100 died. In the City of Sydney 39,000 of its total 104,000 residents went down with the disease and 900 did not recover. In some Sydney suburbs flu reaped an even greater toll. In Alexandria, for example, 50 per cent of all deaths in 1919 were from flu.

The most striking feature of the outbreak and where it differed from previous flu pandemics was that it mainly targeted young healthy adults, particularly those aged from 25 to 39 rather than the very young and the very old as had been the case in previous flu epidemics. In Sydney in 1919, approximately 27 percent of the population were aged between 25 and 39, yet this age group contributed almost half the total flu deaths. Males in particular were susceptible, accounting for 61 percent of all flu deaths. For a society which had witnessed the sacrifice of many of its young men during the World War this must have been a devastating blow. Most of the deaths that occurred were from pneumonia caused by secondary bacterial infections, but the disease could also produce a form of virulent viral pneumonia with haemorrhaging of the lungs leading to death within 48 hours. Serious cases experienced severe headaches and fever, their faces often turned blackish-blue, a sign of cyanosis, they coughed up blood and suffered nose bleeds. Death could be sudden and many collapsed and died within hours, but for most that attack persisted for up to five days.

## Origin and Spread of the Pandemic

It is difficult to pin down the actual origin and beginnings of the influenza pandemic of 1918-19. Most evidence points to the United States where the infection was first recognised in the mid Western States in March 1918. In Kansas an epidemic of influenza broke out on March 5th followed by a wave of pneumonia (Burnet and Clark, 1942, p.69). From here the infection invaded the world probably through the medium of American troops arriving in France. In France it appeared at the beginning of April amongst American troops stationed at Brest and near Bordeaux (Zylberman, 2003, p.192) as well as among American troops near the Swiss border. The infection quickly spread to the local population. Over the next two months it had spread through most of Western Europe in a series of waves. The first wave from May to July was fairly mild. In mid-August the disease mutated and a particularly virulent strain ushered in a destructive phase which lasted until October. More than one million people in Western Europe died from influenza during this period. In America the infection continued its onslaught among the civilian population and by the end of 1918 more than 675,000 had died from its effects.

Aided by the modern system of international travel by steamship and railways, the disease quickly encircled the world. In this it was greatly assisted by the repatriation of many soldiers from Europe to their home countries. Many of the ships carrying troops home to South Africa, Australia and New Zealand called at West Africa en route carrying the infection with them. Within weeks an extraordinary epidemic of influenza spread through cities like Freetown and invaded the surrounding countryside. Within a month more than three per cent of Sierra Leone's population had died (Phillips and Killingray, 2003, p.6). Many ships carrying Australian and New Zealand troops home suffered major epidemic outbreaks on the home voyage. The transport *Chepston Castle*, for example, en route to New Zealand with 1,150 troops on board suffered a major disaster. Seventy-eight percent of all those aboard caught influenza and 83 died before the ship made landfall (Burnet and Clark, 1942, p.71).

Both Australia and New Zealand had experienced moderately severe influenza outbreaks during September and October 1918. In New South Wales 223 deaths occurred from influenza during these months, nearly seven times the average of the preceding five years (Burnet and Clark, 1942, p.73). In the town of Lithgow, for example, 30 people died of influenza during these months but as most deaths were in line with past epidemics, that is, affecting mainly the very young and old, the outbreak did not excite much attention. Perhaps it was a wake-up call, but if so, it went largely unheeded, and apart from some local concern there was relatively little interest.

In late 1918 Australia experienced a stream of ships arriving with a history of influenza aboard on the outward voyage. From late October 1918 until the 30th of January 1919, 326 people suspected of having influenza or who had been in close contact with a case, were formally quarantined at North Head Quarantine Station in Sydney. Of these 326 people, 66 ultimately died. Most of the cases and deaths in quarantine were aged between 20 and 40 years whereas mortality from influenza in the wider community remained generally an issue for the very young and the old. In such an environment the Australian authorities remained largely indifferent, believing that isolation, time, distance and limited local quarantine offered a high degree of security. All that was about to change as the death toll in the Northern Hemisphere continued to mount and the disease continued its deadly sweep around the world. In nearby New Zealand a particularly virulent form of influenza swept the country in November and December 1918 and within only six weeks 8,573 people had been carried away by it (Rice, 2005, p.221). It was without doubt the greatest natural disaster in New Zealand's history. From New Zealand the disease spread to the former German colony of Western Samoa via the medium of infected crew and passengers aboard the inter-island trading ship the Talune. Within a few months more than 8,500 Samoans had perished from influenza, nearly 25 percent of the total population. It was one of the greatest disasters in Pacific history and the highest mortality rate of any country during the pandemic (see Rice, 2005, p.205). The origins of the pandemic in Australia have never been discovered. The first cases on land appeared in Melbourne early in January and it seems clear that the disease must have arrived aboard one of the many ships quarantined in Melbourne harbour. It was the beginning of what was to be one of Australia's greatest natural disasters.

## Diffusion in Time and Space

On the morning of the 25th of January 1919 Sydney residents woke to read in the newspaper of a suspected case of influenza within the city. New South Wales first case of influenza was that of a recently returned serviceman who was admitted to the Military Hospital at Randwick on the 23rd of January. This soldier had stayed in Melbourne for a few days before returning to Sydney by train. His infection was to usher in an epidemic to end all epidemics. Two days after his admission to hospital, three members of the hospital staff who had looked after him developed symptoms of influenza. Over the next few days seven other returned soldiers were admitted to hospital suffering from influenza all of whom had been discharged in Melbourne and then made their own way to Sydney. Following these cases the New South Wales Government advised the Commonwealth Government that New South Wales was officially "infected".

Within a few days other isolated cases began to appear among the civilian population throughout the city, most of who had come from Melbourne or been in contact with someone who had. On the 29th of January a female member of a local theatrical company who had arrived in Sydney from Melbourne fell ill with influenza and was removed to the Coast Hospital. Two days later three other members of the same company also fell ill. In the first week of February more cases began to appear in Sydney and within a week cases began to be noticed in some country areas throughout the State. By early February, 23 cases of influenza had officially been notified in Sydney and over the next month the number of cases increased day by day. While there is no detailed information available on the total number of people who caught influenza during 1919, the temporal course of the epidemic may be judged by examining the distribution of admissions to influenza hospitals as well as the number of deaths from influenza (Figures 3.1 and Figure 3.2). From this material it is clear that the pandemic came in two distinctive waves, the first in mid-April and the second in late June. During March the disease spread slowly but by late March it became apparent that influenza was becoming much more widespread. During early April the disease spread rapidly reaching out from Sydney following the main train lines. By the end of the month influenza had invaded almost every large country town throughout the State. During this time the mining towns of the Lower Hunter were particularly hard hit as were coastal towns like Taree, Coffs Harbour and Grafton and towns like Tamworth, Glen Innes, Gunnedah and Moree in the north and Griffith, Cowra and Cootamundra in the south. While few areas in the State would manage to avoid the pandemic it was the

Sydney Metropolitan area which suffered the most. From the week ending the 5th of April influenza cases began to surge and within five or so weeks, 4,435 people had been admitted to metropolitan hospitals. Thirty-one percent of all hospital admissions for influenza occurred during this period and possibly 23 percent of all deaths. To the relief of many, towards the end of April the number of cases and deaths began to decline giving rise to expectations that the worst was over. But within a few weeks the number of cases and deaths began to rise again and it became clear that another epidemic peak was building. From early June cases and deaths surged to new heights, well above the levels experienced during the first wave in April. In the three weeks after June 7th cases admitted to the Metropolitan Influenza Hospitals reached 3,797 with deaths exceeding 850 in the week ended July 1st.

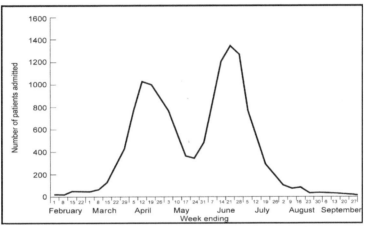

**Figure 3.1** Hospital Admissions to Metropolitan Hospitals for Influenza, 1919.

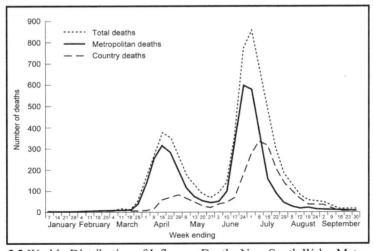

**Figure 3.2** Weekly Distribution of Influenza Deaths New South Wales Metropolitan

and Country Districts, 1919.

The pandemic was most severe in the period from the beginning of the month of June until the 5th of July. During this time there were 5,392 people admitted to hospital suffering from influenza or 38 percent of all hospital admissions during the outbreak. In many ways hospital admissions were simply the official tip of the pandemic iceberg as tens of thousands were ill with influenza throughout the State, most confined to their homes. Deaths as one might expect, lingered a week or so behind admissions. Between the last week in June until mid July more than 3,000 people died from influenza, 49 percent of all deaths during the pandemic.

All in all, the epidemic had come in two waves with peaks in mid April and late June. Together these two waves accounted for 72 percent of all deaths and almost 70 percent of all hospital admissions.

By the time the pandemic was over, 6,244 people in New South Wales had died from influenza including almost 4,000 in Sydney; more than 21,000 people had been hospitalised and approximately 1.5 million had caught the infection. It was without doubt, the pandemic to end all pandemics.

## The Commonwealth Government Response

In late 1918 faced with a pandemic virtually on its doorstep, the Commonwealth Government issued instructions to quarantine all ships where any cases of influenza had occurred on the voyage. All ships arriving from South Africa and New Zealand were to be automatically quarantined for seven days even if there was no evidence of influenza on board. Formal quarantine stations were established at five major entry points to Australia and over the next few months more than 220 vessels would be formally placed into quarantine and more than 58,000 passengers and crew subjected to medical inspection. The S.S. Medic which arrived in Sydney from Wellington in late November provides a good example. The Medic had left Sydney at the beginning of November bound for Europe with a large contingent of Australian troops only to be recalled on Armistice Day. The ship called at Wellington en route home where a number of passengers and crew became infected. By the time the ship had almost reached Sydney influenza had broken out among the troops and crew. On arrival in Sydney there were more than 300 cases of influenza aboard and the ship was placed in quarantine where it remained for almost a month. During this time 25 of those placed in quarantine died, including 13 troops and two nurses.

In addition to its quarantine policy the Commonwealth Government had convened an influenza planning conference for all States and Territories in

Melbourne in late November 1918. The Commonwealth called on all States to agree to a national plan of action if and when an epidemic of influenza broke out in Australia. A 13 point plan was agreed to by all States and Territories including such things as all States accepting their responsibility to notify the Commonwealth the moment influenza broke out within their borders, and that once a State had been formally declared "infected" by the Commonwealth, movement across borders was to be restricted and the Commonwealth would assume full responsibility for inter-state transport movements by land and sea, the quarantine of all borders and the closure of public places. The Commonwealth also urged each State to immediately establish vaccine depots, special influenza hospitals with allied medical staff and supply respirators to the public. In the event of an outbreak of pneumonic influenza a State should also close all places of public resort such as theatres, music halls, picture shows, race meetings, churches and schools, and prohibit all public meetings. A further requirement was that all people wishing to cross State borders would require a health certificate issued by the Commonwealth Government. States such as New South Wales responded by declaring pneumonic influenza a 'notifiable disease' and establishing medical and citizens' consultative committees as well as setting aside a number of beds in public hospitals specifically for influenza cases.

## The Collapse of Cooperation

Over the next few weeks relations between the States and the States and the Commonwealth plummeted as disputes broke out about quarantine and the proper management of the pandemic. New South Wales accused Victoria of not immediately notifying the Commonwealth and other States of its first case of influenza thus allowing the disease time to spread across the border with rail passengers. The Commonwealth was accused of tardiness because the Governor-General did not issue a formal proclamation until February the 5th. Tasmania in an attempt to keep the infection at bay was accused of interfering with interstate trade by placing unfair restrictions on shipping. On the 30th of January the West Australian Government held up the transcontinental train at Parkeston for the quarantine of all passengers even though South Australia had not been declared infected. The next day the New South Wales Government prohibited entry to the State of any person from South Australia. On February the 1st the Queensland Premier contrary to Commonwealth regulations, notified that the border between Queensland and New South Wales would be considered absolute in respect of quarantine with no exception being shown to bona fide Queensland residents. In early February the Queensland Government and the Commonwealth also clashed over the matter of allowing returning troops to be landed in Queensland. Queensland took the matter to the High Court claiming territorial rights but the Court found in favour of the Commonwealth (Plate 3.1). And so it progressed, like an international tennis match with one State serving up official charge after charge, the other, including the Commonwealth returning serve with issues of its own. Adding to the overall problem was that in all States restrictions were continually being applied, relaxed, and then reapplied because of vested interests and public opinion on the one hand, and public panic and hysteria on the other.

In recognition of the fact that that each State, with the exception of Victoria and South Australia, was interpreting the Commonwealth agreement as they saw fit or ignoring it all together, the Commonwealth was forced to either push the agreed regulations and force States to comply, which would result in direct conflict with some States, or withdraw altogether from any attempt to regulate interstate traffic except that which passed between States by sea. In February the Commonwealth officially wrote to all State Premiers stating that Cabinet had decided that as four States had broken away from the terms of the 1918 Agreement that unless the States notify the Commonwealth by noon Wednesday that they would abide by the terms of the Agreement, the Commonwealth would renounce the agreement and would confine its activities to the control of seaborne traffic. No such response came from the States concerned and the 1918 Influenza Agreement lay in tatters, leaving each State to impose its own quarantine and control regulations.

## New South Wales Assumes Control- The Roundabout

Against a background of increasing tension with other states particularly Victoria, and with the Commonwealth 1918 Agreement abandoned, the New South Wales Government went ahead and implemented its own plans to deal with the pandemic. Incensed by Victoria's failure to formally notify the Commonwealth of influenza breaking out, on the 31st of January the New South Wales Premier sent a telegram to the Acting Prime Minister informing him that the outbreak of influenza now becoming evident in New South Wales came from Victoria and that his Government had ordered the closure of all libraries, theatres, schools, churches, public halls and places of indoor resort in the metropolitan district of Sydney. He went on to say:

> "No person residing or being in the State of Victoria shall  pass
> or come into the State of New South Wales, provided  however,
> that any ... bona fide resident of New South Wales   ... residing
> within ... 10 miles of the border ... may return into the State ...
> if he prove to the satisfaction of an officer in charge of police
> in New South Wales and a Government Medical Officer ... that
> he has not during the seven days immediately preceding been in

any district of the State of Victoria where the aforesaid infectious or contagious disease was prevailing… and that he obtain …the certificate that he is not then suffering from the said disease.

All persons within the county of Cumberland, New South Wales, shall after Monday next in public street, vehicle, conveyance, public place, public building, wear a mask completely covering mouth and nose, made of gauze or suitable material, to exclude germs.

No persons in County of Cumberland allowed to congregate in a licensed hotel, bar room, wine saloon, club room, courthouse, court room or other place of public assembly so that air space in above shall become less than two hundred and fifty cubic feet for each person present …" ('Prime Minister's Department, General Correspondence, 1919).

Over the next few months it was like a roundabout. One day severe restrictions on personal movement, as well as on schools, shops and public places were imposed only for the regulations to be relaxed a day or so later, and then reapplied with vigour some days later often in a more severe manner. Sydneysiders must have not known whether they were coming or going as their Government struggled to grapple with a disease about which they understood very little. February 3rd 1919 was officially declared *Mask Day* in Sydney when all residents were expected to wear masks in public. Hundreds of police were placed on mask duty throughout the city and country towns. Two days later 50 people were arrested for riding on the trams with their masks hanging around the necks. All were smokers (*Sydney Morning Herald*, February 5, 1919, p.8). On Mask Day the *Daily Telegraph* ran the following ditty –

*"Beak masks, funny masks,*

*Bag masks and bunny masks,*

*All sorts of gauzy masks worn by me and you.*

*When you see the twinkling eyes*

*Looking almost twice their size,*

*You're sorry that its mask-time*

*If the white mask beats the flu."*

Five days later, the Government relaxed the regulations governing church services, statutory meetings and auction sales by allowing them to be held outdoors under certain circumstances. Three days later and the regulations changed again. Now, no people were allowed to congregate in the County of Cumberland for any form of meeting whether religious, recreational or for any other purpose in any house, building, park, recreation area, street or public place. Church services could be held in the open air provided the clergy wore masks and that all the congregation were spaced at least three feet apart and the clergyman stood at least six feet away from the congregation (*Sydney Morning Herald*, February 15, 1919, p.7). On the 17th of February the Government commenced preparation of the Sports Ground at Albury which was to function as a border Quarantine camp for people wishing to cross the border into New South Wales from Victoria. A number of tents were erected and 40 or so stranded New South Wales residents entering from Victoria were formally quarantined. The Albury camp was divided into three sections to roughly emulate the First Class, Second Class and Steerage structure of the North Head Quarantine Station. At Albury, First Class meals were to be provided at a cost of 10/- per day for the seven day term with the recipient undertaking to repay the amount within three months. Within four days, 164 persons were quarantined in the camp (*Sydney Morning Herald*, February 18, 1919, p.7). Over the next few months conditions in the camp would become a matter of considerable complaint as wet and cold weather allied to overcrowding and for some deplorable living conditions, impacted on those quarantined. In Albury there was also some concern that many of the Quarantine staff left the camp daily and moved at will amidst the town folk. The Mayor of Albury also raised concerns that many country people were avoiding the town for fear of the Quarantine camp and its detainees.

Further to the north, the Queensland Government established its own Border Quarantine camp where people desirous of crossing into Queensland had to spend seven days in quarantine, undergo two inoculations as well as 10 minute stints in the Inhalation Tent three times a day. On February 19th the New South Wales Government decreed that Sunday the 23rd of February would be observed as a Day of Humiliation and Prayer to Almighty God through his divine mercy to avert the approaching disaster (*Sydney Morning Herald*, February 19, 1919, p.7). Many churches held a special mass *"In Times of Pestilence"*. Towards the end of February an air of confidence swept the city as it appeared that the steps taken by the Government and the Department of Public Health had been successful in holding the pandemic at bay. In consequence the Government withdrew the restrictions imposed on open-air meetings and masks now only needed to be worn on public transport. On March 1st the *Sydney Morning Herald* ran the headline-

*RESTRICTIONS ABOLISHED*

-----------------

*NO COMPULSORY MASKING*

---------------

*CHURCH SERVICES TO-MORROW*

-----------------

*THEATRES OPEN NEXT WEEK*

-----------------

*SCHOOLS RESUME ON MONDAY*

and announced that masks were no longer compulsory and that church services, theatres, hotels and picture shows would reopen in a few days time (*Sydney Morning Herald*, March 1, 1919, p.13). Within a week, however, Government confidence in controlling the pandemic was beginning to ebb as the number of cases and deaths continued to climb with every day that passed. It was becoming clear that influenza was assuming a much more threatening and virulent status. On the evening of March the 24th the Premier met with the Medical Consultative Committee to discuss the situation and a decision was made to cancel the Royal Easter Show and to recommend that masks would again be required to be worn by people using all public transport and in lifts.

In the following days the Government also issued regulations prohibiting any person remaining in a hotel bar for more than five minutes and posters were prepared for display inside all bars (*Sydney Morning Herald*, March 27, 1919, p.7). Presumably people avoided hotel bars for fear of infection and bar service became much more rapid and efficient so as to minimize the risk of contact and possible infection. By the beginning of April it was clear to all that the number of cases and deaths was on the rise and a major outbreak was threatening the State.

On the 16th of April a decision was made to close all wholesale and retail shops, other than butchers, bakers, fruit shops and chemists in the metropolitan area. As the epidemic gathered pace and reached a peak in late April the State Government, desperate for any form of control measures proclaimed that no person be allowed to move by car, train or any other vehicle from any area of the State declared infected to any other area 10 miles or more distant unless they complied with all the conditions governing a personal exposure, a medical inspection and medical certificate (*Sydney Morning Herald,* 24 April, 1919, p.7).

A recurring point of confrontation between the Government of New South Wales and the Commonwealth concerned the quarantine of troops returning by ship from Europe, particularly those on ships that had called at Melbourne on their way to the east coast. As a result New South Wales decided to quarantine all such ships arriving from Melbourne for four days followed by a formal medical inspection. On February 10th the New South Wales Premier sent a telegram to the Acting Prime Minister re the troopship Argyllshire which had arrived from Melbourne with more than 1,200 troops aboard, many of whom were injured. The ship was quarantined on arrival in Sydney harbour, and a day or so later a case of influenza was discovered among the troops. Confronted by a period of prolonged quarantine when most simply wanted to return to their families after a long absence, many of the troops rose in revolt and lowered three of the ships boats and escaped. One boat landed at Nielsen Park with 14 men, another at Chouder Head and one with 17 men aboard was prevented from making landfall. Most of those who left the ship were recaptured within a few days but some made it as far as West Maitland and Newcastle before eventually surrendering (*Sydney Morning Herald*, 10 February, 1919, p.6). Transferred to the North Head Quarantine Station, 900 men broke out of the camp and marched to the Manly cargo wharf. At the behest of the military authorities a ferry was sent to collect them and they were transferred to Fort Macquarie from where they all marched to the Sydney Cricket Ground where they would remain for a further three days.

## The Medical Response

In many ways the medical profession were quite unprepared and ill-equipped to deal with the outbreak of influenza. Little was known about viral infections and most believed that they were confronted by a disease of bacterial origin. Antibiotics, which could have prevented many deaths, had not yet been discovered and it would be at least another 34 years before the nature of influenza was better understood. With no specific medical tools to confront the infection, the medical profession were forced to rely on more prosaic measures such as quarantine, isolation, the use of sprays, disinfectants and masks and the banning of public gatherings, as well as simply telling people that at the first sign of symptoms they should go to bed and remain there for at least four days. There is little doubt that public confidence in the medical profession remained at low ebb during the pandemic and was not helped by the way medical practitioners argued among themselves over the origin, nature, cause and mechanisms of spread of the disease. In essence all that the medical profession could offer was palliative and supportive care until the infection had run its course. Largely the medical community used the popular press to disseminate theories and commentaries about the origin, nature and prevention of influenza. Many of the comments made were contradictory and while the medical fraternity struggled to understand the nature of influenza, for many of the public it was much simpler. It was a disease spread by germs and germs came from someone who had been ill or exposed to infection.

In late 1918 a vaccine was prepared from culturing the sputum of influenza patients at the Quarantine Station supplemented by a mixture of streptococcal and staphylococcal material supplied by the Commonwealth Serum Laboratories and by the Professor of Pathology at Sydney University for use against what the medical profession believed was an influenza bacillus. Initially free inoculation of two doses was offered to all people living in the State but such was the public response that supplies were soon overwhelmed and the dose had to be lowered by half. From late November 1918 until mid-May 1919 Public Inoculation Depots began their work throughout the metropolitan area. During this period 1,265 Depots were opened in Sydney and its suburbs. The occurrence of the first case of influenza in the State was followed by an extraordinary stampede to get inoculated which in a matter of days totally overwhelmed the Public Depots. In such circumstances official record keeping broke down as staff struggled to deal with the tens of thousands fighting for a place in the queue. By the end of January 1919, 69,683 people had been inoculated against influenza. Official estimates, which considerably understate the true number seeking to be inoculated, indicate that at least 375,000 inoculations were performed between the 28th of January and the 17th of May 1919. Added to those inoculated in late 1918 this makes a total of 444,683 in the Sydney metropolitan area to which must be added at least 225,000 people outside Sydney and perhaps an additional 150,000 people treated by private medical practitioners throughout the State. This gives an overall total of at least 819,683 but given that until supplies of the vaccine became limited many people received the recommended two doses, this means that in all between 400,000 and 450,000 people sought inoculation – possibly about 25 percent of the State's total population. In Sydney the proportion who sought vaccination was even higher and it is probable that between 35 and 40 percent of the metropolitan population sought inoculation.

But did the inoculation offer any defence against influenza? Unfortunately there is very little follow up evidence apart from some figures for 12,000 patients treated in public hospitals. Of those inoculated, 10.6 percent caught influenza compared to 16.5 percent of those not inoculated but the very small sample, the conditions prevailing in the hospitals, and other intervening variables makes it very difficult to generalise from such figures. Hospital staff, for example, by the very nature of their duties, were undoubtedly more at risk from influenza than the general public. A survey of 752 doctors, nurses and wardsmen in Sydney hospitals, who had been inoculated, revealed that after one month a total of 684 or 91 percent had caught influenza (New South Wales Department of Public Health Report, 1920, p.156). There seems little doubt that the vaccine offered little if any protection particularly for those at high risk of infection. Towards the end of March a new treatment for influenza cases was instituted at the North Head Quarantine Station. This involved the use of calcium lactate in four hourly 15 gram doses as well as vaccine containing 125 million influenza bacilli and 80 million pneumococci. Despite some claims that it provided some success it is highly doubtful whether it offered any protection. ead Quarantine StaionHead

On April the 2nd a Medical Commission set up to investigate the pneumonic influenza epidemic delivered its preliminary report to the State Government under the signature of Welch the Professor of Pathology at Sydney University. Among other things the report stated –

> "... statistics at our disposal tend to show that inoculation  by vaccines does not prevent the spread of the influenza epidemic ... the organisms responsible for the second phase include various groups (a) a pneumococci, and (b) streptococci ,although in some cases the influenza bacillus appears to be the sole cause ... evidence points to the pneumococcus group being the main cause of the second phase ... We recommend the use of pneumococcal vaccine composed of as many different trains as it is possible to secure ..." (*Sydney Morning Herald,* April 3, 1919, p.7).

Initially the medical profession had also supported the use of inhalation chambers across Sydney to provide a thin watery spray of sulphate of zinc as a preventive measure and a number of Inhalatria were established throughout the urban area. Sydney's Tramways Department even fitted out some trams with a system that released a fine spray over passengers. By early April, however, confidence it this measure had like much of the spray, evaporated and the Medical Consultative Committee argued that the procedure was valueless as a preventive measure and urged the Government to abolish all the public Inhalation Chambers. This, the State Government agreed to do the next day.

# The Demographic Impact

There are no official data on the number of people who caught influenza in Australia during 1919. As Armstrong stated in his official report, "It is impossible to state accurately the number of persons who were attacked by influenza ... The number of attacks notified under the Public Health Act was 21,731 consisting of 11,992 in the metropolitan area, 2,558 in the Hunter River District and 7,251 in the remainder of the State. These figures are not even an approximation to the facts." (Armstrong, 1919, p.152). In Sydney, a Government survey of 600 establishments (Banks, Government Departments, City offices, Shops and Factories) involving 106,923 employees found that 36.6 percent had suffered an influenza attack during 1919 (New South Wales Department of Public Health Report, 1920, p.152). There seems little doubt that such employees were more at risk from infection simply because of their day-to-day interaction with members of the public often in fairly constrained office space. The Government Report also indicated that employees in some sectors of the economy, who presumably had much more contact with the general public, suffered much higher infection rates. Bank and insurance office workers, for example, had an attack rate of 54 percent, while for shop workers and merchant office workers the infection rate was 44 percent. While it is difficult to generalise from such figures, it would appear that between 37 and 40 percent of Sydneysiders caught influenza during 1919, roughly between 290,000 and 320,000 people. Quite possibly infection rates were lower in some country areas but some country towns like Lithgow experienced high death rates. Given that only severe pneumonic cases involving lung complications were officially reported, the vast majority of people suffering from influenza went unrecognised. As most people suffered at home and did not seek medical attention, it is very difficult to accurately construct a geographical picture of the epidemic.

Figure 3.3 simply plots the number of officially notified cases as a proportion of the total population in each local government area within Sydney in 1919. Whether the geographical distribution of these severe cases reflects the broader distribution of the disease in 1919 remains debatable, but the map does at least indicate, that apart from Randwick where many returned soldiers suffering from the flu were housed in the Military Hospital, the most severe cases were found in the inner parts of Sydney, particularly Sydney City, Annandale, Petersham and Leichhardt. Sydney's North Shore largely escaped the worst of the pandemic with notification rates well below that experienced in the inner city. To the west of the city, and not shown on the map, Auburn and Lidcombe had the highest rates, 65.7 and 42.3 per 1000 respectively, well above the rates experienced elsewhere in the Sydney region, possibly reflecting the number of cases in the Rookwood Asylum and State Hospital and the Auburn Hospital.

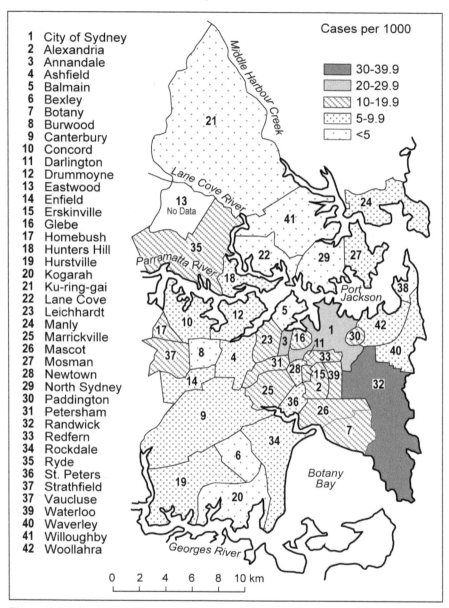

**Figure 3.3** Influenza Notifications Sydney, 1919.

Despite a long history of influenza epidemics in Australia dating back to the 1830s (see Curson, 1985, p.120); the pandemic of 1918-19 had features never before experienced. Earlier influenza pandemics had largely targeted the very young and the very old. By contrast, the 1918-19 pandemic expressly affected healthy young adults aged in their 20s and 30s (Figure 3.4). The

1919 pandemic was particularly severe on people aged from 25 to 39 years. In Sydney this age group made up 27 percent of the total population in 1919 yet contributed 45 percent of all influenza deaths. Fifty-eight percent of all hospital admissions in New South Wales were also aged between 25-39 years as were 58 percent of all deaths that took place in influenza hospitals. Young adult males in particular bore a heavy burden making up 31 percent of all hospital admissions and 40 percent of all hospital deaths from influenza. This was more than double the rate of females in the same age group. Undoubtedly men were more at risk during the pandemic as they made up a high percentage of New South Wales' work force as well as regularly engaging in a wide variety of male dominated social activities in pubs, sporting events, race courses and the like. Of particular note is the fact that for the age group 25-39 the male death rate was virtually double that of females. In total, young adults suffered 2,788 deaths or 45 percent of all deaths from influenza during 1919 and 64 percent of all deaths among those aged 25-39 years were male. Overall the total male death rate was 3.83 deaths per thousand, more than 50 percent higher than the total female death rate. When the age related death rate is compared with the influenza pandemic of 1890-91 in New South Wales it vividly shows how different the 1919 experience was for people of New South Wales (Figure 3.5). In 1890-91 influenza struck down the old, those aged over 60 years, and apart from a small surge of deaths for the very young, deaths at all other age groups were relatively mild. The 1919 experience stands in sharp contrast, with deaths peaking in the young adult age groups.

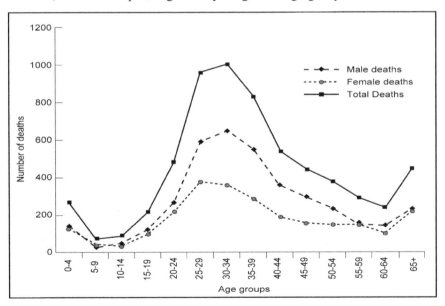

**Figure 3.4** Male and Female Death Rates by Age Group for Influenza, 1919.

What the two pandemics had in common was the experience of middle-aged and older adults where in both cases mortality was high, although nowhere near as high in the 65+ age group as in 1890-91. In 1919 while male deaths took centre stage in some age groups females held their own. For young people aged under 20 male and female death rates were roughly equal and for the age groups 55-59 and 65+ the female death rate exceeded that of males.

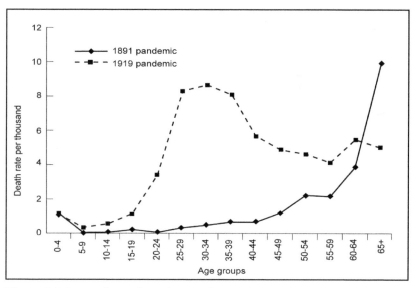

**Figure 3.5** Comparison of Death Rates by Age Group for 1891 and 1919 Influenza Epidemics.

While the influenza pandemic was no respecter of wealth and position, striking down medical practitioners, lawyers and schoolteachers as well as government workers, shopkeepers and labourers, there was still a degree of socio-economic differentiation in the victims it selected, with lower class groups suffering a higher rate of mortality. Table 3.1 provides a broad oversight of this mortality differential. There seems little doubt that those in occupations which brought them into everyday contact with fellow workers and the public were more at risk. So too were the poor living in dilapidated and overcrowded homes where children intermingled with neighbours in the street.

Influenza affected every aspect of life in Australia. In New South Wales more than 5,000 marriages were torn apart by the death of one or both partners and many children found themselves bereft of one or both parents. Fear of infection also seems to have influenced people's decision to marry and have children. Data from Sydney reveals that many marriages were postponed at the height of the pandemic despite the return of many thousands of troops from overseas (Figure 3.6). It seems that the marriage boom that was expected to follow the return of young men from overseas was delayed by at least some months as people contemplated the raging pandemic. The pandemic may also have resulted in a delay of conceptions and birth as families waited out the worst of the pandemic.

| **Table 3.1:** Mortality Rate from Influenza by Occupational Group. New South Wales Males Aged 15+ | |
|---|---|
| **Death Rate per 1,000** | |
| Labourer | 12.0 |
| Transport Worker (Harbour, Rivers and Sea) | 7.8 |
| Transport Workers (Roads) | 6.4 |
| Industrial Worker | 6.2 |
| Domestic Worker | 6.0 |
| Rail/Tramway Worker | 5.9 |
| Postal/Telegraph Worker | 5.5 |
| Commercial | 4.8 |
| Professional | 4.3 |
| Primary Producer | 2.4 |
| | |
| Source: McCracken and Curson, 2003, Table 8.2. | |

As Figure 3.7 shows there was a significant deficit of births throughout 1919 although much of this was undoubtedly related to the absence of many young men overseas. The baby-boom which was expected to follow close on their return seems to have been delayed by some months until after May 1920. Not only did people postpone marriage and birth during the peak of the pandemic but at least 1,400 women of childbearing age died of influenza during 1919. In Sydney, official records show that 224 pregnant women were admitted to influenza hospitals, 60 of whom died and just over half had their pregnancy terminated by the attack of influenza (New South Wales Department of Public Health Report, 1920, p.147).

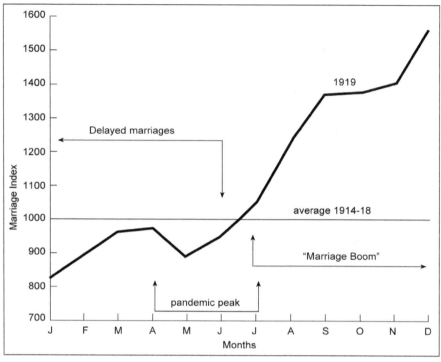

**Figure 3.6** Impact of Influenza Epidemic on Marriages in Metropolitan Sydney. 1919.

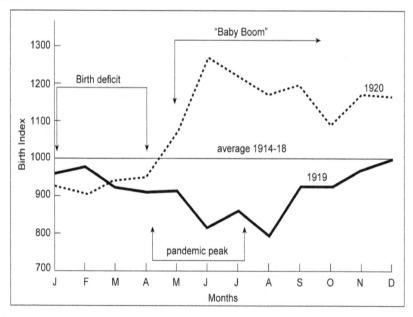

**Figure 3.7** Impact of Influenza Epidemic on Births in Metropolitan Sydney, 1919-1920.

## Caring for the Victims

At the onset of the pandemic New South Wales possessed no more than 2,000 available hospital beds. Between January and September 1919 more than 21,000 people were hospitalised suffering from severe influenza, many in hastily established temporary emergency hospitals staffed by volunteers (Plate 3.2). Many Sydney firms and organisations agreed to their premises being used for such purposes including Anthony Horden and Sons, the Vacuum Oil Company, Lasaght Brothers, Lindeman Wines and Colonial Mutual Insurance. Other influenza patients were accommodated in temporary hospitals set up in the premises of the Royal Agricultural Society, the Randwick Race Course as well as in many kindergartens, church halls and public school buildings. In country areas temporary hospitals were set up in whatever buildings were at hand including the Bush Nursing School at Hillgrove, the School of Arts and Show Grounds at Casino and the West Maitland Benevolent Home. Hospital admissions peaked in mid April. In one week alone at the height of the pandemic, 1,300 people were admitted to hospitals throughout New South Wales. In total, almost 2,644 people in New South Wales died of influenza after being admitted to hospital (Plate 3.3).

The majority of deaths occurred in metropolitan hospitals. Overall the death rate was approximately 15 percent of all those admitted to Sydney hospitals compared with a figure of 8.9 percent in country hospitals. A few country hospitals did, however, experience very high death rates. The emergency hospital established in the Lithgow District School saw 169 patients admitted with influenza of which 56 or 33 percent died in the hospital, while in the Broken Hill District Hospital the death rate from influenza was more than 19 percent. The bulk of people stricken with the disease in New South Wales remained at home and relied on home visits to provide everyday support. Many, however, remained totally isolated and struggled to survive. In November 1918 with a view to handling any epidemic that might arise, the New South Wales Government had established a Citizens' Influenza Administration Committee comprised of city businessmen and women. When the epidemic broke out the Committee assumed responsibility for organising measures to relieve the distress arising from unemployment as well as providing help and assistance for 'contacts' quarantined in their homes (Plates 3.4 and 3.5). Up until June 1919 the relationship between the Committee and Health Department officials remained fraught and considerable friction developed over what role the Committee should assume during the epidemic. On at least three occasions the Citizens' Committee offered its resignation to the Premier but were eventually persuaded to continue their work when a new agreement was reached. In an attempt to provide support for those confined to their homes the New South Wales Government also established a Home Nursing and District Depot service, closed many schools and called for volunteers. Within a few months 100 such depots were established with a staff of 1,800 of whom 1,200 were volunteers. House visits were organised to infected homes to provide much needed food, clothing, blankets and medicines. People were encouraged to display a large *SOS* card in their front window if help or support was desperately required. There seems little doubt that such cards when displayed must have added to the wave of fear and panic that swept through many neighbourhoods. Understandably in such circumstances, the Government found it extremely difficult to find volunteers willing to visit the ill in infected homes. Many women refused to volunteer arguing that their primary responsibility lay with caring for their own families and many expressed a deep-seated fear of catching the flu themselves.

Doctors and nurses too, were in short supply largely because many were still away serving with the Australian forces in Europe. In their absence many 4th and 5th year medical students and young girls came forward and volunteered to help. Many volunteers were unable to return to their own homes for fear of taking the disease with them and infecting their own families. The care of young children provided a particular problem particularly where their parents were ill with flu, had died, or had been removed to hospital. In such circumstances most of their relatives and friends were understandably reluctant to intervene for fear of becoming exposed to the infection. Confronted by this dilemma, the Society for the Welfare of Mothers and Babies stepped into the breach and agreed to take over responsibility for caring for destitute or uncared for young children. Cronulla House, a large cottage by the sea-side and a number of Kindergarten buildings were placed at the Society's disposal and the children were looked after by girl volunteers. In total, 595 young children were accommodated in one or other of these emergency hostels during the pandemic including 100 aged less than one year.

## The Press

Throughout the course of the pandemic the press played a pivotal role in presenting information and moulding public opinion. Every New South Wales newspaper carried daily reports of how many hospital admissions and deaths had occurred from influenza as well as what measures the Government and medical profession had put in place to contain the outbreak. Regular reports were also provided of influenza in all country towns and districts. The press coverage of the pandemic evolved through a number of stages. In late 1918 most papers contained small reports of the pandemic's impact and progress through Europe and the USA. By late 1918 attention had shifted to New Zealand and the need to quarantine all ships entering Australian ports.

## Public Reaction- Fear, Panic and Hysteria

People avoided trams and ferries, declined to go to church services, the pub or sporting events and avoided walking on city streets. For weeks the Sydney Domain was virtually deserted. People also tried to flee from Sydney. The afternoon before the Government restrictions on movement came into force, people crowded on to long distance trains at Central Station in an attempt to get away (*Sydney Morning Herald*, February 7th, 1919, p.5). Flu swept through most neighbourhoods, swamping streets with few homes escaping its ravages. Neighbours avoided neighbours for fear of infection and when flu was known to have broken out in a particular street or block of flats, locals barricaded themselves inside their own homes and refused any contact or support. In cases where a whole family had succumbed to flu the house was locally branded as one to be avoided at all costs. Fear and panic spread to the workforce and business community. Undertakers were reported to be refusing to touch dead bodies for fear of infection (*Daily Telegraph*, April 9th, 1919, p.8). Tramway employees demanded a "pandemic pay increase", to keep them at work, and on the afternoon of February 10th the Sydney Branch of the Waterside Workers Federation refused to assemble for work on the wharf side for fear of infection (*Sydney Morning Herald*, February 11th, 1919, p.7).

In the countryside fear was widespread and visitors from Sydney were shunned and exposed to discrimination as being the purveyors of infection. The experience of a city visitor to Albion Park sums up how the local community responded. The visitor, a female business representative arrived in Albion Park only to be subjected to derogatory comments and the refusal of any hotel to offer accommodation. People stood well back from her at the first hotel she visited and she was told that there was no accommodation available. Word quickly got around and at the next hotel she tried, two scared looking young women waved her away with the remark that they had no rooms available. Another woman who entered the hotel at this moment turned and ran for her life. Eventually, having been turned away from every hotel in the town the woman went to the police station and told them that as a bona fide traveller she demanded accommodation. The police then accompanied her to one of the hotels and reminded the owner of the terms of his licence and the woman was finally admitted with no good grace. Later the woman approached the owner of a local farmhouse but he implored her to keep away or his property would be placed into "quarantine" by the local community (*Sydney Morning Herald*, April 19th, 1919, p.12). There was also a view across the State that non-whites were more susceptible to influenza. Such a view was bolstered by reports of the high death rate among Blacks in South Africa, Maoris in New Zealand and Western Samoans. In some parts of New South Wales this resulted in discriminatory practices aimed at the Aboriginal population such as in Kalgoorlie where fringe dwelling Aboriginals were driven away from the town into the desert.

## The Impact on the Economy

Influenza impacted heavily on New South Wales's government services and the State's business sector. Every business house in Sydney, every public institution and utility struggled to carry on normal business behaviour with severely depleted staff numbers. With more than a one third of Sydney's population ill with the disease, shops, restaurants, government offices and businesses struggled to stay open with restricted workforces and the fact that many of the public were either ill or reluctant to enter such premises for fear of infection. The high level of infection and the fear of public places saw many refuse to venture into shops, businesses or government offices.

On the 7th of February the *Sydney Morning Herald* claimed that more than 18,000 people had been thrown out of work because of the Government's influenza precautions, including 6,000 picture show workers, 5,000 liquor trade workers, 2,000 shop assistants and 15,000 wharf labourers (*Sydney Morning Herald*, 7th February, 1919, p.7). In late June 1,100 postal workers were ill with influenza as were many staff employed by the Electrical Light Services and City Council workers. On June 15th more than 300 hundred tramway workers were absent from work, and by late June 6,000 rail and tramway workers were absent from work throughout New South Wales including more than 4,000 in Sydney (*Daily Telegraph*, June 25, 1919, p.8). The pandemic also took a heavy toll of bank employees. The English, Scottish and Australian Bank had 40 percent of its staff absent from work in the week preceding June 12th and the Union Bank had one-third of all it employees absent ill *(Daily Telegraph*, 12 June, 1919, p.6). It was not only businesses that suffered as many Court sittings and Government committees throughout New South Wales were also cancelled.

## Popular Cures and Advertising

It is perhaps a truism that during times of crisis there are always those quick to take advantage and to seek to benefit from widespread community fear and panic. In the case of the influenza pandemic this was the case particularly when doctors and medical services could offer little respite or possible cure. During the period from January until October 1919, the purveyors of popular medicines and quack cures had a virtual field day and were quick to cash in on public anxiety and insecurity. In New South Wales newspapers were full of advertisements for every sort of product claiming to offer a sure defence and protection against the symptoms of the flu. Dr Morse's Indian Root Pills, Nicolas Aspro Tablets, Clements Tonic, Bonox Fluid Beef, Chamberlain's Cough Remedy, Bonnington's Irish Moss, Glaxo, Heenzo Cough Diamonds, and Lifebuoys Soap, were just some of the many products that were widely canvassed in the daily press claiming to offer sure protection against the symptoms of influenza (Plate 3.6). Patent medicines and quack cures held sway throughout the pandemic, a sign of growing fear and uncertainty. Not to be left behind, many businesses ran adverts claiming that their particular product offered a sure defence against influenza. Ozmanette pyjamas and nightdresses, for example, were canvassed as offering warmth and nocturnal protection as was Warns Wonder Wool, highly recommended as saving thousands of lives in New Zealand during the recent pandemic, with its magic wrap and medicated cotton-wool fibres. Even men's suits were canvassed as in the advertisement *"Dodge the flu by wearing a J.P.J.Suit"*. By April Sydney's newspapers were literally full of advertisements claiming to offer a sure defence or cure against the flu such as the *"Russell"* system of painless tooth extraction removing the danger that decayed teeth meant for contracting flu, or the advertisement to buy a motorcycle a sure way of keeping you out of *"germ-haunted trains and trams"*. Alcohol was widely canvassed as preventative against infection and face masks were sold all over Sydney. Kodak marketed its cameras with the slogan – *"No Shows, No Races, No Theatres- No Picture Shows. One thing remains – the beautiful hobby of Kodak Photography"*.

In Sydney many departmental stores claimed to offer shoppers protection due to their policy of regular fumigation. McCathies Ltd, for example, claimed that their store was fumigated every day and offered a safe shopping environment. Grace Brothers went further and offered all their shoppers a visit to the store Inhalatorium Chamber which would ensure protection from influenza for at least 24 hours. Other businesses advertised that all their staff had been inoculated and wore masks. David Jones and other departmental stores offered enhanced mail and telephone systems to allow people to shop without actually visiting the store. Others went further and saw the pandemic as an opportunity for personal gain, such as the two men who posed as official Health Inspectors going from house to house offering to spray people with a special anti-flu spray for the princely sum of 2/6 to 5/- (*Daily Telegraph*, April 14, 1919, p.6).

## Conclusion

The 1919 influenza pandemic ranks as the greatest social and health disaster in Australian history. Overall, millions succumbed to flu during the first half of 1919 and 15,000 died from the disease. In New South Wales more than

6,000 died from the flu during 1919. The pandemic came in two major waves, the second far more devastating that the first. No explanation of this has been advanced save the possibility that the virus mutated. Overall, the pace of the spread of the disease took Australia by surprise and totally overwhelmed the response capacity at every level of society striking fear and panic throughout the Australian community.

CHAPTER 4

# The Bite is On! The 1925-26 Dengue Epidemic

## Introduction

Dengue remains one of the major vector-borne viral threats to world health. By the mid 1990s an estimated 2.5 billion people worldwide were regularly exposed to the infection and today, up to 100 million cases occur every year. A world pandemic of dengue commenced soon after the end of World War Two and by the 1980s had spread to involve Papua-New Guinea and much of the Western Pacific (see Guard, et al, 1984). Dengue, in Australia, however, has a much longer lineage. First reported in Northern Queensland in the 1870s, there is a long history of epidemic outbreaks, mainly in Queensland, but often spreading to involve northern New South Wales. After a number of outbreaks in the 1950s, dengue was thought to have disappeared, from Australia until a major epidemic in Townsville in 1981-82, whereafter dengue resumed its place as a major public health problem in Queensland. Since 1870, dengue has been responsible for almost 1,000 deaths in Australia and more than one million cases of illness.

The 1925-26 dengue epidemic remains one of the most significant and geographically widespread episodes of infectious disease in Australia's history. In a little over four months, it caused 147 deaths, more than a half a million cases and spread to involve much of Queensland and Northern New South Wales. Broad contemporary estimates suggest that between 70 and 80 percent of the population of affected areas caught the disease and the epidemic had a major impact on all aspects of everyday life. In eastern Australia, the greatest impact fell upon people living in towns and cities, isolated farms and rural areas largely escaping, except where their inhabitants paid visits to local towns. In some towns, more than 85 percent of the total population was affected by the disease. Generally, the epidemic caused a major dislocation to social and economic life, producing tremendous human suffering and remains to this day, one of Australia's most significant vector-borne morbidity crises. This study of the 1925-26 dengue epidemic is not simply an exercise in the historical geography of disease. Dengue remains to this day a major threat to Australia's public health, particularly in parts of Northern Queensland where epidemics are common, and the potential for the disease to spread to other parts of eastern, northern and north-western Australia, remains very real.

Climate change may also affect the current distribution of the disease by influencing the life cycle and current distribution of the vector. This chapter argues that, not only do we need studies that model and statistically predict the potential distribution of disease agents and vectors, but that we also need information on how societies respond and react to epidemiologic crises and how human behaviour ultimately influences disease distributions. Reconstruction of this particular epidemic may also provide us with clues about the distribution of vector-borne disease in the future, particularly in the context of changing social and environmental circumstances. The main purpose of looking back at this epidemic therefore, is to assess how dengue spread across time and space, its demographic and socio-economic impact, and how well prepared and flexible Australian society was in dealing with an epidemiologic disaster of such magnitude. Such information provides us with a valuable insight into how our fellows in time and space faced the challenge of infectious disease, and how societies and their members behaved during times of epidemic crisis.

A basic aim of this chapter is to reconstruct the progress, impact, effects of, and reactions to, a major epidemic of dengue in Australia in 1925-26. This is a study of an infectious disease event designed to reconstruct the various environmental factors contributing to a major social and epidemiological crisis. To this end, it is hoped to shed some light on future infectious disease outbreaks by way of analogy. This analogy works at a variety of levels. At one level, analogies can be drawn between the particular environmental circumstances of the 1925-26 epidemic and possible future environmental circumstances. At another level, reconstruction of patterns of human behaviour and community reaction may lead to conclusions about future community behaviour when confronted by a future infectious disease crisis.

## Dengue

Dengue is an acute febrile disease caused by infection with a flavivirus of the Toga virus family transmitted by the bite of an infected mosquito usually of the *Aedes aegypti* species. The dengue virus occurs as four sub types designated DF1, 2, 3 and 4. Endemic throughout much of the tropical world, dengue is usually regarded as a debilitating illness of relatively short duration with a high attack rate but low mortality. Typical uncomplicated dengue is a biphasic illness with an incubation period of between three and 15 days, characterised by fever, headache, retro-orbital pain, lumbar backache and severe pains in the muscles and joints. In classical dengue, onset is sudden and the fever usually lasts for 48-96 hours, subsiding only to briefly reprise. This is followed by a characteristic red rash which appears usually on the trunk and extremities but avoids the face. The acute illness phase lasts for approximately seven days and one attack confers immunity to the particular sub type. Recovery is generally complete, although convalescence may take several weeks. Dengue Hemorrhagic Fever (DHF) usually strikes young children and involves internal bleeding sometimes culminating in Dengue Shock Syndrome (DSS), followed by collapse and in a number of cases, death. Currently, only classical dengue fever is found in Australia, although there would appear to have been cases of DHF during the 1897-98 epidemic in Queensland (See Hare, 1898).

## The Vector

In Australia there would appear to be at least three potential mosquito vectors of dengue, *Aedes aegypti, Ae. scutellaris, and Ae. katherinensis* (the last two found only in Northern Australia). *Ae. aegypti* is the vector of most concern in Australia because of its widespread distribution (particularly in the past), and because of its adaptation to living with human populations. Historically Australian researchers played an important role in unravelling the epidemiology of dengue and in particular the role played by the vector. Bancroft, in the early part of this century was the first to suggest that *Ae. aegypti* was the vector of dengue (Bancroft, 1906), while a decade later, Cleland *et.al* demonstrated conclusively that *Ae. aegypti* was the principal vector concerned (Cleland *et.al,* 1918). *Ae. aegypti* is typically a *container-breeder* which has become virtually dependent upon humans in that it is principally confined to human-manufactured larval habitats, such as rainwater tanks, drums, tins, old tyres, blocked roof guttering, plastic cartons, vases, plates and bird-baths (Plate 4.1). Water storage and type of water supply are, therefore, key factors contributing to the life-cycle and distribution of the vector. The maintenance of *Ae. aegypti* is dependent upon five basic factors: (a) obtaining a blood meal by the female adult without which eggs will not be formed, (b) the availability of a moist surface on which the eggs can be deposited, (c) the presence of water suitable for larval life, (d) a temperature conducive to the completion of the life cycle, and, (e) shelter from predators during the larval and adult stages. For the adult insect, activity and longevity are related to the existence of suitable humidity, shelter and access to drinking water. Such conditions as these are normally found in the neighbourhood of human populations. In the 1920s, (as in the more remote parts of Northern Australia today), domestic water containers/tanks, the cistern, flower pots/saucers and shaded rooms with cupboards and hanging clothes, provided a conducive environment for the species to breed and proliferate. Mosquito population numbers are also affected by the types of larval sites available. These sites influence not only the density of mosquito populations but also the nutritional status of the larvae which in turn has implications for vector size, survival, and longevity. *Ae. aegypti* lays its eggs as single units and deposits them on a moist surface such as a rock, the inside of a container or tree hole, or into soil crevasses and/or drying mud. Such eggs can survive long periods of desiccation until subsequently inundated when water level rises from rain/flood during which they hatch. A suitable temperature, an adequate supply of water and a suitable container in which to breed, are all critical factors in the life cycle of the mosquito. There is thus a close association between rainfall and the disease, although heavy rainfall may have the immediate effect of washing away many larvae. Heavy rain may often be followed by a lag of a month or two before the breeding cycle is complete. In ideal water temperatures (20-25°C), the period from maturation of eggs to emergence of the adult insect and its first blood meal, is from 16 to 30 days. In colder temperatures, this cycle may increase to up to 45 days. The minimum temperature for species survival would seem to be between 10 and 12°C, although the species may survive during lower outdoor temperatures by seeking refuge in the warmer micro-climate of indoor environments. It would also seem that the egg may be resistant to low temperatures and that the species can over-winter in the egg stage. Temperature also influences the vector's life-cycle as well as virus replication. Temperatures around 30°C tend to speed up these processes. Temperature, rainfall and humidity would, therefore, seem to act as a selective pressure on *Ae. aegypti* populations. Long periods of drought and hot temperatures may kill off many eggs, allowing only a few to hatch following flooding. Location of the breeding container and the water supply would appear critical in this equation. Containers located inside buildings which are continually refilled, provide a more conducive breeding environment than those located outdoors, subject to the vagaries of the outdoor environment.

The origins of *Ae. aegypti* in Australia are open to debate. It is possible that the species arrived on Australia's Northern coast prior to European settlement with Malay voyagers. Equally possible, the species may have accompanied the immigration of gold miners and other immigrants to Queensland in the 1860s and 1870s. Gold was discovered at Ravenswood and Charters Towers in 1869-71 and Townsville rapidly developed as a major port serving the gold centres (Kay *et al,* 1987). It is likely that the mosquito and dengue became entrenched in the Townsville-Charters Towers region during this period. There are also a number of references to passengers suffering from dengue arriving at east coast ports in the late 19th century. Whatever the route or means of establishment, by the 1890s there seems little doubt that *Ae. aegypti was* quite widely distributed over Eastern Australia. Figure 4.1 attempts to reconstruct the geographical distribution of *Ae. aegypti* between 1897 and 1993 from epidemic accounts and mosquito surveys. From this Figure it is clear that *Ae. aegypti* had a widespread distribution throughout Northern Australia, Western Australia, Queensland and New South Wales over the last 100 or so years.

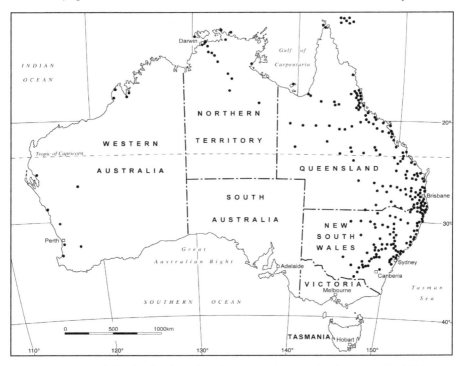

**Figure 4.1** Recorded Distribution of Aedes Aegypti Mosquito in Australia, 1893-1993.

Since 1950, however, the geographical distribution of the species has substantially contracted to parts of Northern Queensland (Figure 4.2). Dengue, by contrast, probably followed a pattern of periodic multiple invasions from outside Australia, mimicking the ebb and flow of immigration in the period after 1866 and kept active in human-Aedes-human cycles until disappearing when environmental conditions became unfavourable and/or when immunity levels rose substantially. It may also be that the disease became endemic in parts of Queensland between 1870 and 1943. Once established in and around the major ports, *Ae. aegypti* would have been easily transported along rail, road and coastal shipping routes. While the species has always exhibited a limited flight pattern, it has often been a most willing passenger over long distance journeys. The common forms of land and sea transport prior to the 1950s encouraged the diffusion of the vector over large distances. Rail transport in particular, provided both a vehicle and a ready and sympathetic environment for vector proliferation and diffusion. Coastal shipping, particularly prior to the 1930s, also played an important role in this process.

## The History of Dengue Epidemics in Australia

Since the 1870s, dengue epidemics have been a regular feature of the Australian public health scene. Some of the most extensive epidemics of dengue in the developed world have occurred in Australia since the end of last century, including nine major epidemics between 1897 and 1993 (Table 4. 1 and Figure 4.3). Most of these outbreaks have been confined to Queensland, Northern and North-western Australia, although on a number of occasions, epidemics have extended beyond Queensland to Northern New South Wales. The first reference to major dengue outbreaks occur in the last three decades of the 19th century including epidemics at Charters Towers (1870s and 1885), Townsville (1879 and 1895) as well as cases as far afield as Sydney in 1886, in this case, probably introduced from infected travellers from New Caledonia.

In late 1897, an epidemic of dengue commenced in Cooktown, in Northern Queensland, and subsequently spread to involve most coastal towns and cities and as far inland as Hughenden. By early the following year the disease had spread to encompass most of the towns and cities in Southern Queensland as well as parts of Northern New South Wales. The epidemic was very severe, producing 184 deaths and in some coastal Queensland towns between 70 and 80 percent of the population were affected (Figure 4.4). In Brisbane it is estimated that 40 percent of the population had dengue in 1898 (Hirschfeld, 1898). Five years later, in the summer of 1904-05, Australia experienced one of its most severe epidemics of dengue. Extending over most of the towns and cities of Queensland and Northern New South Wales, this epidemic caused more than 200 deaths in Queensland, including 94 in Brisbane alone. During this epidemic, it is estimated that 75 percent of the population living in affected areas caught the disease including between 90,000 and 100,000 people in

The 1925-26 Dengue Epidemic

Brisbane. The epidemic produced cases as far afield as Sydney and had a tremendous impact on Australian social and economic life. Evidence from various employment agencies and institutions in Brisbane suggest an overall attack rate in excess of 80 percent with some employers/institutions having rates of more than 90 percent (Table 4.2). Figure 4.5 provides an overview of the number of deaths that occurred in Queensland from dengue between 1895 and 1926.

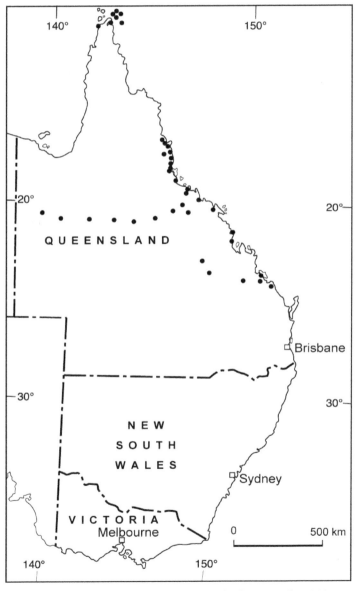

**Figure 4.2** Distribution of Aedes Aegypti Mosquito in Australia 1993.

Deadly Encounters

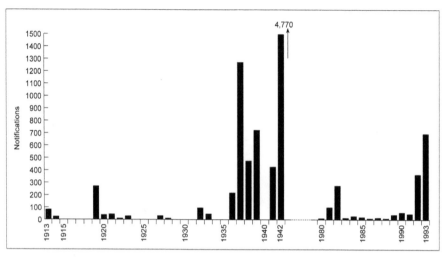

**Figure 4.3** Notification of Dengue Cases in Australia, 1913-1993.

| Table 4.1: Major Dengue Outbreaks Australia 1879-1993 | | |
|---|---|---|
| Year | Location | Estimate of Cases |
| 1879 | Townsville | |
| 1885 | Rockhampton/Charters Towers | 1,500 |
| 1886 | Sydney | |
| 1894 | Thursday Island | 500 |
| 1895 | Townsville | 3,000 |
| 1897-98 | Queensland/Northern NSW | 40,000 |
| 1899 | Queensland | |
| 1901 | Queensland | |
| 1904-05 | Queensland/Northern NSW | 120,000 |
| 1908 | Northern Queensland | |
| 1909-10 | North-West Australia | 10,000 |
| 1910-11 | Queensland/Northern NSW | 8,000 |
| 1913 | Western Australia | |
| 1914 | Northern Territory | |
| 1916 | Queensland/Northern NSW | 5,000 |
| 1919 | Western Australia | 2,000 |
| 1925-26 | Queensland/Northern NSW | 560,000 |

| 1927-28 | Darwin/Northern Territory | |
| | | |
| 1936 | Northern Territory | 1,000 |
| 1937-38 | Townsville/Northern Queensland | |
| 1939-40 | Northern Territory | 3,000 |
| 1941-43 | Northern Territory/ Queensland/ Northern NSW | 40,000 |
| 1953-55 | Northern Queensland | 20,000 |
| 1958-59 | Northern Territory | |
| 1981-82 | Northern Queensland | 3,500 |
| 1990 | Townsville/Cairns | |
| 1992-93 | Northern Queensland | 25,000 |

**Table 4.2:** Dengue Cases: Brisbane Workers And Institutional Population, 1904-5 Epidemic

| Institution | Total Population | Total Number Attacked | Attack Rate |
|---|---|---|---|
| Staff 3 Hospitals | 74 | 66 | 89.2 |
| Retail/wholesale Butchers | 124 | 114 | 91.9 |
| Retail/Wholesale Wool combers* | 42 | 30 | 71.4 |
| City Warehouse Staff | 483 | 432 | 94.4 |
| City Clothing Factory Staff | 471 | 435 | 92.4 |
| Newspaper Literary Staff | 30 | 28 | 93.3 |
| Grammar School Staff & Boarders | 41 | 40 | 97.6 |
| City Bank employees | 76 | 62 | 81.6 |
| Gas Works - Outdoor employees | 48 | 31 | 64.6 |
| Public Service+ | 993 | 732 | 73.7 |
| Railways - Office Staff | 96 | 87 | 90.6 |
| Tramways - Drivers/Conductors | 347 | 311 | 89.6 |
| Hospital for Sick Children - Resident Staff | 41 | 36 | 87.8 |
| Diamentina Hospital - Resident Staff | 26 | 23 | 88.5 |

| Diamentina Hospital -Patients | 79 | 51 | 64.6 |
| Boggo Rd Gaol - Warders | 17 | 15 | 88.2 |
| Boggo Rd Gaol - Prisoners | 195 | 61 | 31.3 |
| **Total** | 3183 | 2554 | 80.24 |

| + Excluding Education and Railway Departments |
| * Belmont |
| Source: Aust.Med. Gazette, 1905. |

Australia's next major epidemic of dengue occurred in the summer of 1910-11 primarily in Southern Queensland but affecting all the coastal towns between Rockhampton to Murwillumbah in Northern New South Wales. More than 100 Queenslanders perished during this epidemic. This was followed by a major outbreak in 1916 which extended over much of Queensland as well as to a number of north coast towns in New South Wales. The disease's spread in this case, was in many ways facilitated by the movement of soldiers and recruits from the military camp in Brisbane (Goldsmid, 1916). The incidence of the disease on the population was very heavy and social and business life suffered accordingly.

In the summer of 1925-26 there developed the most geographically extensive epidemic of dengue in Australia's history. By early 1926 this epidemic had extended all over Queensland as far south as Sydney, and as far west as Bourke in New South Wales. In only four months, 147 deaths occurred and it is estimated that approximately 560,000 people suffered from the disease during the period from November 1925 to June 1926 (See Figure 4.4).

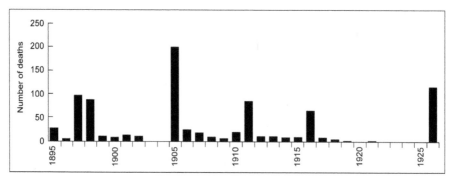

**Figure 4.4** Number of Recorded Dengue Deaths in Queensland, 1895-1926.

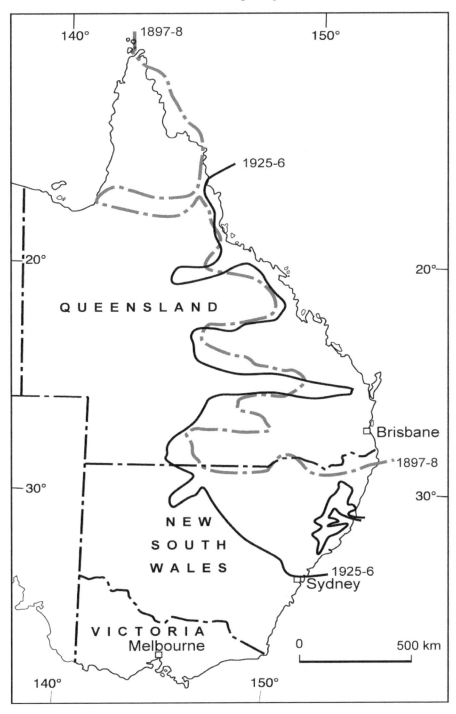

**Figure 4.5** Spatial Extent of Dengue Epidemics of 1897-1898 and 1925-1926.

In the years after 1926 there were small but regular dengue outbreaks in the Northern Territory and Northern Queensland. These outbreaks culminated in a major epidemic between 1941-43 which extended over much of Northern Australia, Queensland and Northern New South Wales. While only 5,000 cases were officially notified many hundreds of thousands of people were swept up in the epidemic with 80 to 85 percent of the population affected in some areas. After 1943, Australia was thought to be largely free of indigenous dengue until 1953-55 when a major outbreak occurred in Townsville producing at least 15,000 cases and extending from Rockhampton west to Barcaldine and south to Gladstone and Biloela (Kay *et al*, 1984). More than 25 years then elapsed before the next outbreak of the disease in 1981-82 when approximately 3,000 cases occurred in Northern Queensland. Finally, in 1992-93 another major epidemic broke out in Townsville and Charters Towers in Queensland involving almost 25,000 cases.

## The 1925-26 Epidemic

### Environmental Receptivity

There seems little doubt that environmental conditions in eastern Australia in 1925-26 were very conducive to the survival and proliferation of *Ae. aegypti*. In the first place, *Ae. aegypti* was widely distributed over most of the settled areas of Queensland and the northern half of New South Wales. In the second place, the combination of warm to hot temperatures, spring and summer rain including very heavy downpours and flooding in parts of coastal northern Queensland and Northern New South Wales during the period November 1925 - April 1926 would have provided ideal breeding conditions. Thirdly, the human environment and the many available breeding places associated with the The lack of notification data for dengue in Australia until the 1980s makes it very difficult to fully assess both the temporal frame and demographic impacts of this or other epidemics. From contemporary accounts it seems clear that the epidemic commenced in North Queensland in the latter part of 1925 and from there, spread in the ensuing months to engulf much of Queensland and Northern New South Wales. If the temporal pattern of mortality is indicative of the course of the epidemic, then the disease reached its peak in March and April when 60 percent of all deaths occurred (Figure 4.6).

The 1925-26 Dengue Epidemic

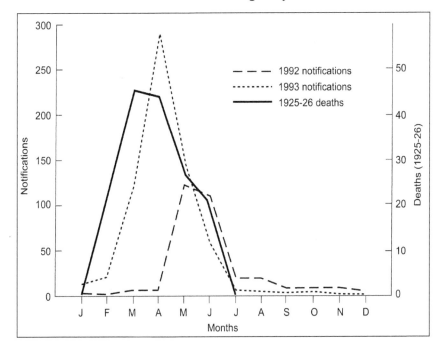

**Figure 4.6** Monthly Distribution of Dengue Notifications and Deaths 1925-1926 and 1992-1993

## Patterns and Mechanisms of Diffusion

The 1925-26 epidemic commenced in Northern Queensland sometime in October or November 1925 and from there spread to involve much of the state and Northern New South Wales in the first few months of 1926. By May 1926, the epidemic had extended over much of closely settled Queensland and Northern New South Wales. The southern-most boundary of the epidemic extended in a line west from Sydney to just south of Bourke, southwest to Tilpa, and thence northwards to the Queensland border. In 1926, just over 800,000 people lived within this area. Interestingly, part of the New England plateau seems to have been totally bypassed by the epidemic, and towns like Walcha, Armidale, Uralla and Glen Innes experienced no dengue cases while all around them the epidemic raged. It would seem that this area was protected by its elevation (about 915 metres above sea level), and that this was above the temperature/altitude threshold of *Ae. aegypti.*

Nearby towns below an altitude of 915 metres such as Tamworth (about 600 metres above sea level), suffered many thousands of cases. Within New South Wales, the towns of the North-western Slopes and Plains bore the real brunt of the epidemic as did areas in the Tweed, Clarence and Hunter River districts. The epidemic invaded New South Wales by a variety of routes. The north coast area of Tweed Heads and Murwillumbah was invaded from southern Queensland in late 1925 even though the epidemic in these areas did not reach its peak until early 1926 (Figure 4.7). Regular population movements across the Queensland-New South Wales border plus regular coastal shipping services were responsible for much of the spatial diffusion of the epidemic. This allied to the widespread distribution and high prevalence *of Ae. aegypti* through both states explains much of the disease's geographical distribution in 1925-26 (Figure 4.8). The epidemic in Bourke and surrounding districts illustrates one element of this diffusion process at the local level (Figure 4.9). Bourke was probably infected from Cunnamulla in Queensland when a local bookmaker returned home from the Cunnamulla races in January, as well as by infected Queensland visitors to the Bourke races in early February. It would seem that from these contacts local mosquitoes took up the infection and spread it widely within the town. Many of the race visitors had stayed at one or other of Bourke's major hotels and within a week of the race meeting, most of the residents and staff of these hotels were sick with dengue. By the second week of February, Bourke was in the grip or a major epidemic. In the next three months, possibly as many as 1,400 of Bourke's total population of 1,560 caught dengue. The epidemic was undoubtedly assisted by the fact that Bourke supported a large mosquito population in 1926 including many *Ae. aegypti.*

Surveys carried out during the epidemic revealed heavy infestations of *Ae. aegypti* in the many breeding sites around the centre of the town. In most cases these included infected water tanks and ant pots around the town's major hotels. Rainwater tanks were used at all hotels and better class houses. These tanks were usually cylindrical galvanised-iron types with a perforated cover. In no case was the tank rendered mosquito-proof by wire-meshing. Mosquitoes also commonly bred in the sullage water pit at the hospital, in horse troughs and in fire buckets. From Bourke, the epidemic spread quickly to surrounding towns and districts. Many people from outlying areas had the misfortune to be infected by virtue of their routine everyday connections with Bourke. Others were unlucky enough to have attended the Bourke race meeting in early February.

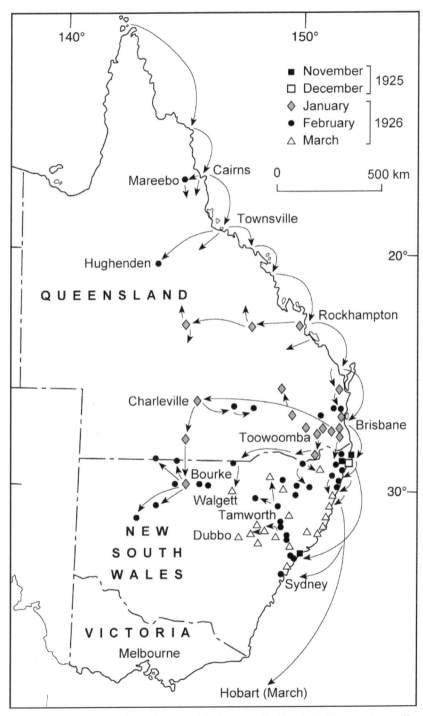

**Figure 4.7** Spatial Diffusion of 1925-1926 Dengue Epidemic in Eastern Australia.

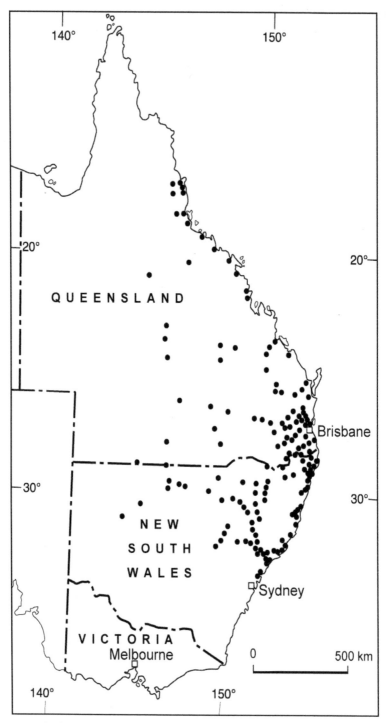

**Figure 4.8** Distribution of Aedes Aegypti during 1925-1926 Epidemic.

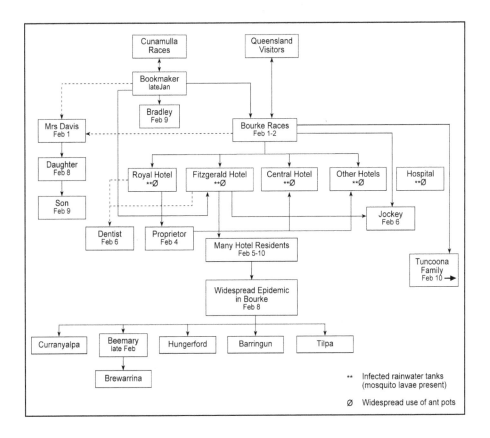

**Figure 4.9** Diffusion of Dengue Epidemic in Bourke During 1926.

In Queensland the epidemic spread along the major railway lines, travellers often being infected in one town, developing the disease in another and then infecting local mosquitoes and thus starting a fresh outbreak of the disease. Rail transport also transported mosquitoes over long distances as well as providing short-term harbourage and many suitable breeding sites. Dengue in 1925-26 tended to closely follow long-distance train routes often initially bypassing intermediate towns in favour of long distance transfer to rail termini. Thus, the disease leapt from Brisbane to Charleville, intermediate stations being infected at a later date. In like fashion, dengue spread from Rockhampton to Emerald and from there to Barcaldine. From Barcaldine a number of neighbouring towns were infected. An additional diffusion route saw dengue accompany passengers and mosquitoes aboard the many coastal steamers plying the Queensland and Northern New South Wales coast. In Newcastle, the first cases of dengue occurred as early as the end of November 1925 in the vicinity of a Stockton shipbuilding yard where several boats trading to the Northern Rivers area where laid up on the slip for maintenance. *Ae. aegypti* were said to be plentiful in the district and the subsequent epidemic in the surrounding districts probably originated from this focus.

## Demographic and Social Impacts

Like many of the earlier epidemics, the 1925-26 dengue outbreak had a major impact on life in Queensland and New South Wales. Overall, 147 deaths occurred during the epidemic, 116 in Queensland and 31 in New South Wales. In general, the housebound were most at risk during the epidemic with the majority of deaths being children under the age of 5 years and elderly persons over 65. In total, these two categories accounted for almost 60 percent of all dengue deaths during 1925-26 (Figure 4.10). Contemporary estimates of morbidity during the epidemic suggest approximately 560,000 cases of dengue based on the fact that roughly 70 percent of the population was affected. Writing a few years after the epidemic, Sutton estimated that 75 percent of all school children in Queensland had caught dengue in the 1920s (Sutton, 1931). Table 4.3 selectively estimates the demographic impact of the epidemic on a number of towns and districts in Queensland and New South Wales. Overall, while perhaps between 70 and 80 percent of the population in areas affected by the epidemic caught dengue, the impact on particular communities varied, dependent to a large extent upon the degree of geographical isolation, frequency of contact with nearby towns and railway stations, and the extent to which anti-mosquito campaigns were put in place and carried through. Hence in Kyogle in Northern New South Wales, only about 10-15 percent of the local population was affected, while in neighbouring towns the proportion was nearer 90 percent. Kyogle enjoyed the benefit of fairly extensive anti-mosquito procedures within the town dating back to 1923.

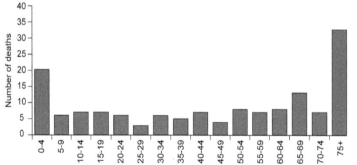

**Figure 4.10** Deaths from Dengue by Age and Sex in Queensland and New South Wales, 1915-1926.

**Table 4.3:** Demographic Impact of 1925-26 Dengue Epidemic, Selected Towns and Districts

| Town/City/District | Population Affected |
|---|---|
| Mareeba | "25% of all school children ill" |
| Maryborough | c. 9000 cases |
| Hughenden | "dengue raging in town" (March) |
| Crows Nest | "most households visited by disease" |
| Texas | "dengue raging" (February-March) |
| Cooray | "staff of practically every business house affected" |
| Yarraman | "dengue epidemic raging, hardly a family having escaped its ravages" (late March) |
| Murwillumbah | "more than 90% of the population affected". 3-4000 cases |
| Kyogle | "10-15% of population affected" (February) |
| Lismore | "more than 85% of population affected" (January) |
| Nambour | "30% of schoolchildren absent" "all staff of Maroochydore Shire Council off work ill" (first week of March) |
| Casino | "c.50% of population affected" |
| Pomona | "c.50% of population affected" |
| Bourke | "c.90% of residents affected" |
| Imbil | "hardly a family escaped" |
| Singleton | "majority of inhabitants affected" |
| West Maitland | "several hundred cases" |
| Tamworth | "at least 2000 cases" |
| Queensland/Northern NSW | "70-80% of population affected in localities touched by the epidemic" "possibly 90% of population affected in towns, down to 10-15% in more isolated rural areas" |
| Queensland | "75% of all schoolchildren affected"    (Sutton, 1931:614) |

Source: Comments drawn from local newspapers, 1925-26.

Figure 4.11 displays those localities in Eastern Australia that experienced cases of dengue during the epidemic. It is clear that the epidemic was largely concentrated in South Queensland, to the south and south west of Bundaberg and from there to Charleville and Barringun with a further arm extending between Cairns and Bundaberg with extensions to towns along the main rail and road routes to Hughenden, Barcaldine, Blackall and Bileola. The epidemic also extended into New South Wales, with many towns in the north east of the State affected. Within this broad area, the epidemic impacted heaviest upon those living in towns and cities where the attack rate was as high as 85-90 percent. Isolated farms, stations and communities suffered far less, with attack rates as low as 10 percent, and many of these people had the misfortune to be infected whilst visiting local towns for either business or social purposes. In some towns only a handful of households escaped the ravages of the disease.

In Bourke, approximately 90 percent of the town's population caught dengue between February and April, in Lismore more than 85 percent were affected, while in Murwillumbah, there were approximately 4,000 cases involving roughly 90 percent of the total population. Most schools and businesses were affected, the ranks of the public service severely depleted, and for some months, business and public affairs in many parts of Queensland and Northern New South Wales virtually ground to a halt. Law Courts had to adjourn hearing cases, hospitals suffered from a shortage of trained staff and postal and telephone services were severely curtailed. Many Government Departments were forced to close early or offer restricted services from February to April, and the Education Departments of both states had difficulty in maintaining a teaching staff up to adequate strength. In any particular week in the period from late February until early April, at least 25 to 30 percent of school children were absent from school. The medical profession and hospital staff were not spared the effects of the epidemic. In Casino, more than 60 percent of the nursing staff at the District Hospital was ill in mid-March, while in many areas the local doctors were included among those struck down by the disease.

The epidemic also severely disrupted normal economic activities in many rural districts, and shearing activities in parts of Queensland such as Charleville were severely disrupted. For many businesses, the economic loss in sales and productivity must have been a major set back. For three months in 1926, normal business activities in parts of Eastern Australia virtually ground to a halt. Table 4.4 illustrates the impact of the epidemic on nine major businesses trading in Brisbane during 1926. Loss in wages stemming from staff absences exceeded £4,000.00, a not inconsiderable sum in 1926. Overall, about 27 percent of all employees in these firms were ill during the epidemic. No figures are available on the effect of the epidemic on production, sales and profits, but it must have been substantial. If figures from the 1904-05 epidemic in Brisbane are any guide, then most people would have been absent from work for up to two weeks during the acute phase of their infection. A return to full health would have presumably taken much longer and undoubtedly many returned to work and school still suffering from the aftermath of the infection. Small businesses were among the hardest hit by the epidemic. Many were forced to close their doors during February, March and April.

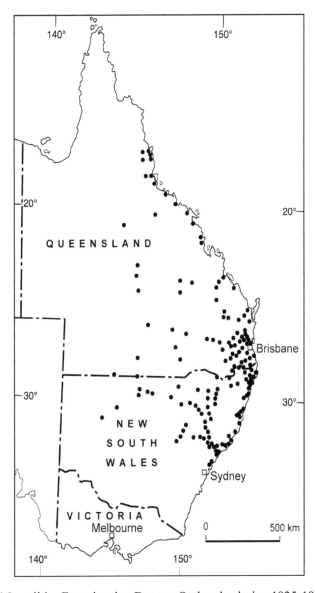

**Figure 4.11** Localities Experiencing Dengue Outbreaks during 1925-1926.

**Table 4.4:** Percent of Employees Attacked And Loss in Wages during Dengue Epidemic In Brisbane, January to mid April 1925-6

| Firm (No.) | % of Employees Affected | Loss in Wages (£) |
|---|---|---|
| 1 | 65.6 | 438.23 |
| 2 | 23.8 | 569.13 |
| 3 | 17.0 | 213.87 |
| 4 | 20.0 | 200.00 |
| 5 | 20.0 | 220.00 |
| 6 | 26.0 | 303.00 |
| 7 | 35.0 | 500.00 |
| 8 | 24.0 | 130.00 |
| 9 | 15.3 | 1451.00 |
| Total | | 4,025.23 |
| | | |
| Source: Hamlyn-Harris, 1931:27. | | |

## War on Mosquitoes!

In 1925-26 it was well recognised that mosquitoes were the vectors of dengue. The major measure advanced by local authorities and public health authorities to control the epidemic was a planned and concentrated campaign targeting mosquitoes. From January 1926 various local authorities proclaimed a *"War on Mosquitoes"* and commenced a process of surveying potential mosquito breeding sites such as unscreened water tanks and standing pools of stagnant water. In New South Wales, Local Government Ordinance 41 was proclaimed in many towns and districts which provided local authorities with the power to enforce the eradication of mosquitoes by the removal of rubbish from yards and public places, the screening of water tanks and the suitable control of all standing water. Ordinance 41 also provided the authority for local government inspectors to carry out house by house inspections, as well as providing the power to prosecute any householder upon whose premises mosquitoes were found to be breeding.

In parts of New South Wales considerable efforts were made to put Ordinance 41 into effect by screening private and public water tanks and/or covering standing water containers such as horse troughs with a surface layer of kerosene or paraffin. Pools of surface water were also regularly oiled. House to house inspections were also widely undertaken in both Queensland

and New South Wales with the aim of identifying and removing potential mosquito breeding sites. Campaigns were instituted to drain areas of standing water and notices were served to residents where such pools of water had been identified. In achieving these aims, local authorities had to combat vested interest, disinterest, outright opposition, backsliding and the generally poor state of housing, rubbish removal and urban sanitation.

There is a long history in Australia of people resenting rules and regulations that impinge on individual rights and freedoms even when such rules are in the interests of public health. In Maryborough, for example, housing inspectors found that only about 25 percent of all homes in 1926 possessed screened water tanks. In other areas, local communities either refused to adopt Ordinance 41 or if they did, did so in a half-hearted way. In West Maitland, for example, the local Council refused to adopt any anti-mosquito measures and the town suffered several hundred cases of dengue in consequence. In Singleton, Alderman O'Halloran attempted to move at a Council meeting in April, that Ordinance 41 be enforced, but his vote was the only one in favour of the motion. This was the case despite the fact that most households in the town had been visited by the disease in the previous month. In Newcastle, the City Council organised a *"Mosquito Week"* in January 1926 which included lectures on dengue, the epidemic and the importance of controlling mosquitoes as well as practical demonstrations of screening and mosquito control. In the second week of March, the Brisbane City Council moved to introduce a major mosquito eradication scheme. The aim was to appoint a scientifically-trained investigator and team charged with the responsibility of planning and carrying out a systematic mosquito eradication campaign within the city. In March, Dr. Hamlyn-Harris and a team of four household inspectors, one scientific clerk, and four unskilled workers for cleaning and spraying work, were appointed. In addition, funds were made available for scientific and control equipment. The appointments did not go ahead without some degree of acrimony among Council members about the costs involved and the financial burden on ratepayers. Over the next few months this team commenced a major campaign to identify and remove mosquito breeding sites in inner Brisbane. In addition, Dr. Hamlyn-Harris organised a major public education campaign involving public lectures, pamphlets and regular newspaper reports and articles. Despite such efforts, it would appear that conditions quickly slipped back to something approaching pre-epidemic conditions. Records of a survey of more than 1600 homes in inner Brisbane carried out the year after the epidemic indicates that between 47 and 71 percent of all homes needed attention to remove potential mosquito breeding sites and that mosquito larvae were present in between 25 to 53 percent of all homes, including *Ae. aegypti* in 16 to 36 percent (Table 4.5).

| Table 4.5: House Inspections Inner Brisbane March and October 1927 | | | | |
|---|---|---|---|---|
| Areas* | Total Homes | Needing Control (%) | **Aedes aegypti Larvae Present (%)** | **Mosquito Larvae Present (%)** |
| Area 1 | 572 | 51.7 | 35.8 | 53.0 |
| Area 2 | 520 | 70.6 | 21.9 | 40.0 |
| Area 3 | 522 | 47.1 | 16.1 | 25.5 |
| **Total** | 1614 | 56.3 | 25.0 | 40.0 |
| | | | | |
| *March Inspections | | | | |

**Area 1**
South side of City comprised of 25% business premises, 20% boarding houses, flats and 55% middle-class homes.

**Area 2**
Close to heart of City comprised of 20% business premises, 10% boarding houses, flats and 70% small private homes.

**Area 3**
Primary residential area, 60% detached homes, many in poorer areas without water tanks.

Source: Hamlyn-Harris, 1931.

## Commercial Reactions

While commercial and public life suffered a major setback because of staff absences due to illness during the epidemic, business houses were not slow to appreciate the commercial advantages offered by the outbreak. The purveyors of popular medicines and health tonics had a field day. At the height of the epidemic, the Queensland and New South Wales newspapers were full of advertisements extolling the virtues of a variety of products as curatives or preventatives against dengue. Tonics, such as Clements Tonic and Geddes No. 1 Medicine, were widely canvassed as essential remedies (see Plates 4.2 and 4.3). Equally, popular analgesics like ASPRO were widely advertised as a means of controlling the fever associated with an attack of the disease. Beverages ranging from Pure Unadulterated Orange Juice to Blue Jacket Rum were also advertised as restoratives following an attack. The manufacturers of anti-mosquito products also advocated the merits of their products with great zeal. The manufacturers of pump sprays such as FLY-TOX (almost an icon in Australia and New Zealand!) must have reaped a bonanza in profits as sales of their products soared.

## Signposting the Future

Up until the late 1940s dengue outbreaks were a regular and widespread feature of life throughout parts of Australia. Despite the deaths of almost 1,000 Australians from dengue during this period, in terms of their impact on the general population, these outbreaks were fairly mild and the disease became to be seen, not as a serious impediment, but rather as a more-or-less ubiquitous feature of life, characteristic of certain parts of Australia (Plate 4.4). People rarely fear what is commonplace and for the most part not deadly. Equally, people will only consider modifying their health behaviour when disease is severe and life-threatening (Haefner and Kirscht, 1970). Hence it is not surprising, that as soon as one epidemic of dengue passed, old patterns of behaviour returned.

The geographical retreat of *Ae. aegypti* to parts of Northern Queensland after 1943 would not seem to be related in any way to climatic factors but more to a number of important changes in technology and human behaviour. These included the extension of reticulated water supplies and the decline of domestic water storage tanks, the emergence of refrigeration as an alternative to Coolgarde safes as a means of keeping food cool and fresh, and the related disappearance of ant pots. In addition, the replacement of steam trains by diesel (from the 1970s), with the disappearance of fire buckets and water tanks from all railway stations, the decline in coastal shipping as a major means of transporting goods and people, as well as increased surveillance and anti-mosquito campaigns and the widespread use of insecticides, all played an important part. These changes removed many potential breeding sites as well as helped reduce local mosquito populations. The advent of the backyard motor mower also allowed the easier management of backyard environments. In New South Wales, the distribution of *Ae. aegypti* seems to have substantially retreated since the late 1940s and the 1925-26 epidemic was the last occasion when the vector had a widespread distribution throughout the State.

Some things have changed in Australia since the 1925-26 dengue epidemic, others have not. The opportunity for container breeding such as in backyard and public-place rubbish, blocked roof guttering and other water containers remains very high in both Queensland and New South Wales. Surveys in Townsville for example, reveal a very high percentage of *Ae. aegypti* associated with indoor and greenhouse plants, in saucers of water under pot plants, as well as with a variety of water-holding receptacles such as tyres, drums, blocked roof gutters and bird baths (Kay et al., 1987). It would also appear that the discarded plastic container now plays the role that the fire bucket, ant pot or water tank played in the 1920s, providing a receptive environment for mosquito breeding. Throughout its history in Australia Ae. *aegypti* has tended to follow the path of human settlement. The recent pattern of population movement to more remote rural blocks in Queensland and the Northern Territory and the re-introduction of rain-water tanks may hold considerable significance for the future distribution of the species. Further, prolonged periods of drought and/or water shortage in parts of eastern Australia could easily see the reappearance of rainwater storage tanks both as a means of garden water supplies and for other purposes. Under such circumstances the potential for a re-introduction of the species from Queensland to New South Wales remains a possibility.

The incidence of dengue around the world has increased dramatically over the last few decades with recorded cases increasing from just half a million in 2000 to well over five million today. Dengue is now endemic in more than 100 countries throughout the world with the Americas, South-East Asia, and the Western Pacific regions being the most seriously affected. Asia represents about 70 percent of the global burden of dengue with considerable implications for Australia. Dengue is also spreading through parts of Europe. The spread of dengue is closely related to human mobility, population density, and access to reliable water sources as well as to methods of water storage. In the past, as previously mentioned, the dengue mosquito, *Aedes aegypti*, was found across Queensland, in parts of the Northern Territory, as well as in parts of New South Wales, and so Australia still suffers the chance of major dengue outbreaks occurring.

# CHAPTER 5

# A Crippling Burden:
# Polio 1903 - 1962

Polio occupies a unique place in Australian history. It came and went in a little over half a century and left an indelible imprint on the Australian way of life and national psyche. The long hot polio summers deeply influenced how Australians regarded disease, pain and suffering and for lengthy periods the nation was hostage to panic, fear, hysteria and terror. For over 50 years, until the advent of the Salk vaccine in the mid 1950s, the disease seemingly struck at random, afflicting both rich and poor, city and rural dweller and transformed Australia. The only thing sufferers had in common was that they were largely children or young adults. For 50 years, fear of polio would be woven into the national experience. From the second decade of the 20th century, polio was regarded as a fierce monster, lurking in the dark hollows of human experience, waiting to carry off otherwise healthy young children, many from middle class backgrounds. This frightening imagery, nurtured by the popular media, helped shape the response of generations of Australians. The climate of fear constructed around polio, was undoubtedly heightened by the increasing frequency and apparent randomness of epidemics as the century progressed, particularly among middle class families living in more comfortable circumstances, and by the apparent inability of medical science to provide a cure. The history of polio in Australia is really the history of how fear transformed a whole society. No one could predict the next epidemic or where or who the disease might next strike. No one had any real idea as to how to lessen its impact or prevent its tragic toll. Such a situation bred fear, panic and distrust. Many schools and theatres were closed and swimming pools shunned for fear of contagion. Gatherings of children were prohibited, even in churches and Sunday Schools. People were forbidden to go to work. Children were forbidden to move from one part of Australia to another. Neighbours shunned neighbours. Parents dreaded a child crying in the night or a child who seemed out of sorts. Strict quarantine procedures were installed between the Australian states and relatives of victims were often ostracized and denied access to their place of work.

The medical profession largely supported immobilization of the limbs of paralysed patients despite the often fierce opposition of people like Sister Elizabeth Kenny who advocated hot packs and keeping the limbs active. The purveyors of popular medicines preyed on the fearful and desperate. While polio often killed, it was the image of the paralysed child on crutches, in a wheelchair or the dreaded iron lung, which transfixed the nation. To live during a polio epidemic was to live through an all-pervading environment of fear and uncertainty. And then suddenly the threat disappeared. The introduction of the Salk vaccine in 1956 followed by the Sabin vaccine ten years later, transformed the disease scene. By the mid 1960s polio had all but disappeared as an infectious disease threat in Australia. The story of polio, like that of many epidemic diseases, reveals many things about Australia and Australian society. It revealed the best and the worst in Australia and while the conquest of polio illustrates the ultimate triumph of medical science over infectious disease, it is at the level of individual and community suffering that polio had its greatest impact. The disease also had a major effect in terms of hospitalization, quarantine and prevention.

The disease had a shattering effect on many young lives. The often lengthy period of splinted treatment, the confinement and lack of company, deprived many young children of a normal childhood and adolescence as well as involvement in the usual educational and socialization processes of schooling. The often long separation from parents and friends allied to the rigidity of hospital rules and procedures, where children in infectious wards could not be touched or approached and often only viewed from afar, placed a terrible burden on families. Within the polio wards, the often frightening hospital procedures of lumbar punctures, chloroform, respirators and the dreaded iron lung, added to the pain and discomfit of splinting and immobilization, plus the monotony and drabness of hospital food, made life uncomfortable for most, and terrifying for many (Plate 5.1).

Such enforced seclusion and treatment was compounded by the social isolation, ridicule and stigmatisation that accompanied any return to formal schooling or the workplace. Survivors were condemned to an ostracised life, sequestered away from mainstream society as cripples, deformed outcastes, shut off from their friends and largely removed from the normal routines and activities of everyday life. Even rehabilitation held its own terrors. The pain from long immobilized muscles and nerves subjected to regular physiotherapy was for many, almost too much to bear. Health workers too, were not spared the opprobrium poured out on sufferers. During the 1937-38 Tasmanian epidemic, nurses and other hospital workers involved in nursing polio cases were advised not to tell neighbours and friends what they did for fear of repercussions (see Killalea, 1995, p.95).

## The History of Polio Epidemics in Australia

Polio was without doubt one of the most devastating infectious diseases to affect Australia during the first 50 years of the 20th century. Probably between 25,000 and 40,000 Australians had the misfortunate to catch the disease during the first half of the century. The number of Australians who caught the disease but only exhibited minor symptoms was most likely to have been in excess of 100,000. Many who caught polio adapted to the infection and managed to lead productive and happy lives. Others suffered greatly and laboured under residual paralysis. Australia has experienced some of the most severe polio epidemics in the developed world, particularly in the period 1937-54. At least three outbreaks rank among the most severe ever recorded – the 1937-38 Tasmanian epidemic, the epidemic in Victoria during the same years, and the epidemic which raged in South Australia between 1950 and 1951. In addition, epidemics in Queensland in 1951 and New South Wales in 1950-51 were also significant. While sporadic cases of polio probably occurred throughout the 19th century, by the turn of the 20th century the disease had begun to assume a more epidemic frame and within a few decades had become one of the most feared diseases. The first recorded epidemic of polio occurred in Port Lincoln in 1895 when 14 cases were reported. A more extensive epidemic commenced in Sydney in the summer months of 1903–04, eventually extending across New South Wales and to all other States, except Tasmania. In all, 34 cases were recorded in Sydney, but there were at least 20 cases recorded from other parts of the State, all young children under ten years of age. The epidemic spread to Queensland during 1904, with 108 cases recorded among young children. In Queensland, the epidemic spread from the southern border of the State in a northerly direction. As well as Brisbane, cases were recorded in Toowoomba, Ipswich, Maryborough and Townsville.

During April, May, and June of 1908 an extensive epidemic broke out in Victoria, the majority of cases occurring in the more densely populated inner suburbs of Melbourne. In total, 135 cases and six deaths were recorded (Stephens, 1908). Minor outbreaks continued over the next few years with cases recorded in Bendigo, Sydney and Tasmania. It would appear that from a return of cases treated at the Royal Alexandria Hospital for Children in Sydney for the period 1891-1913, that there was a notable surge in cases after 1909, particularly in 1912-13 (see Cleland and Ferguson, 1914, pp. 312-319). Probably, this reflects more the increased availability of children's hospital cots than any rapid increase in the incidence of the disease. Nonetheless, in 1913, there were 50 children in the Royal Alexandria Hospital being treated for infantile paralysis. Between 1915 and 1918 there were major epidemics in Queensland (1915), New South Wales (1916) and Victoria (1918) totalling almost 1,200 recorded cases. Figures 5.1 and 5.2 trace the history of polio cases in Australia and various states from the second decade of the 20th century through to the early 1960s. Over the next 40 years, Australia was to experience at least half a dozen major epidemic periods of poliomyelitis, culminating in the extensive outbreaks of the 1949-56 period. A number of these epidemic encounters stand out in Australian history (Tables 5.1 and 5.2).

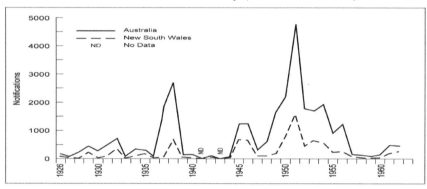

**Figure 5.1** Polio Notifications in Australia and New South Wales, 1926-1962.

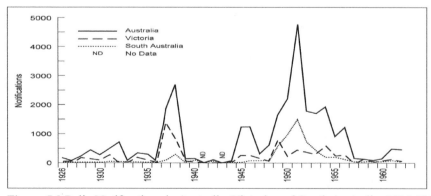

**Figure 5.2** Polio Notifications in Australia, Victoria and South Australia, 1926-1962.

# A Crippling Burden: Polio 1903 -1962

In 1931-32 New South Wales experienced a major outbreak but one that paled in comparison with what was to take place in Victoria and Tasmania five years later. In both cases the epidemics represent the deadliest polio outbreaks in both States' history. Australia experienced another major epidemic in 1945-46, principally in New South Wales where there were more than 1,300 cases. In 1949 Australia entered a new phase of polio epidemics and the next eight years would see a series of traumatic episodes with major epidemics in New South Wales, South Australia and Queensland in 1950-51, and in New South Wales, Victoria and South Australia between 1952 and 1954. Between 1949 and 1954 more than 16,000 Australians succumbed to the disease and as official figures do not include very mild paralysis cases, the total was quite probably well in excess of 30,000. The turning point came in 1956 following the introduction of the Salk vaccine and a major vaccination campaign commencing in the latter part of the year and although 1,194 cases of polio were officially reported in 1956, by the following year, the number of cases had fallen to only 125.

**Table 5.1:** Major Outbreaks of Poliomyelitis in Australia, 1900 – 1962

| Year | Total | Comments |
|------|-------|----------|
| 1904 | 108 | Qld 108 |
| 1908 | 135 | Vic 135 |
| 1915 | 395 | Qld 332 |
| 1916 | 414 | NSW 311 |
| 1918 | 388 | Vic 303 |
| 1929 | 436 | NSW 240, Vic 144 |
| 1931-32 | 1,181 | NSW 488, Qld 329, Vic 303 |
| 1937-38 | 4,555 | Vic 2176, Tas 1006, NSW 757 |
| 1945-46 | 1,300 | NSW 1324, Vic 485, Qld 448 |
| 1949-54 | 13,92 | SA 4293, NSW 4146, Vic 2584, Qld 1656, WA 731, Tas 480 |
| 1950-51 | c.6,000 | SA 2428, NSW 2351, Qld 1136, Vic 635 |
| 1953-54 | 3,583 | NSW 1192, Vic 853, SA 574, WA 480 |
| 1955-56 | 2,068 | Vic 486, NSW 462, WA 434, SA 304, Qld 302 |
| 1961-62 | 893 | NSW 421, Qld 294 |

Source: Author, State Health Reports, Commonwealth of Australia Official Year-books.

**Table 5.2:** The Most Severe Polio Epidemics

| State | Year | Cases | Rate per 100,000 |
|---|---|---|---|
| 1. Tasmania | 1937-38 | 1,006 | 421 |
| 2. South Aust | 1950-51 | 2,428 | 342 |
| 3. Victoria | 1937-38 | 2,176 | 135 |
| 4. Tasmania | 1951-52 | 271 | 87 |
| 5. Queensland | 1951 | 1,030 | 83 |
| 6. NSW | 1950-51 | 2,351 | 71 |

Source: Author, State Health Reports, Commonwealth of Australia Official Year-books.

**Table 5.3:** Age Structure Polio Cases in NSW 1915-24

| | Age Groups | | | | | | |
|---|---|---|---|---|---|---|---|
| | Under 1 | 1-4 | 5-14 | 15-21 | 25+ | NS | Total |
| Sydney | 126 | 249 | 91 | 20 | 5 | 2 | 493 |
| Rest of NSW | 32 | 188 | 88 | 13 | 4 | 0 | 325 |
| Total NSW | 158 | 437 | 179 | 33 | 9 | 2 | 181 |

Source: Cumpston, 19: 327.

## The 1931-32 New South Wales Epidemic

Generally, the incidence of polio was fairly high throughout Australia in the period between 1928 and 1932, with local epidemics in New South Wales and Victoria in 1929 and 1931-32, in Queensland, 1932 and Tasmania in 1930. An epidemic broke out in New South Wales during the summer and autumn of 1931-32. The epidemic extended to Victoria and to Queensland with only a scatter of cases in other states. In total, 1,189 cases of polio were notified during 1931-32, 435 of which were in New South Wales. Almost 200 cases

100

occurred within the Sydney metropolitan Area, with the rest scattered across the State. As Figure 5.3 illustrates, the epidemic peaked in late December 1931 and early January the following year, and ended towards the end of May 1932. In Sydney the epidemic began six weeks earlier than in other parts of the State and peaked about one month earlier.

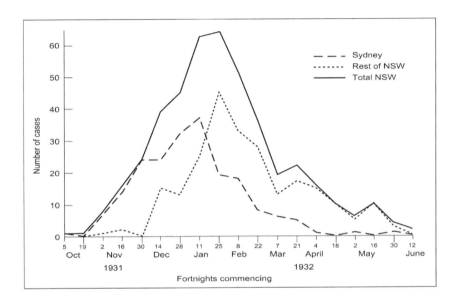

**Figure 5.3** Fortnightly Distribution of Polio Cases in Sydney and New South Wales, 1931-1932 Epidemic.

As Figure 5.4 indicates, the bulk of cases were young children with almost three quarters of all cases reported being aged under nine years. Most initially suffered a mild illness accompanied by some vomiting, followed by headaches, neck, back and limb pain and often stiffness in the neck and spine. In 1931-32 it was still thought that the route of infection was through the nose and throat, by the inhalation of infected dust and the consumption of infected food and that the disease was spread directly by nose and mouth secretions, from others who had the disease, from convalescent patients, and indirectly from soiled clothing, food, including milk, dust and by insects. To prevent infection people were urged to disinfect and burn any nasal or intestinal discharges and to thoroughly boil and disinfect any items of clothing or bedding used by a patient.

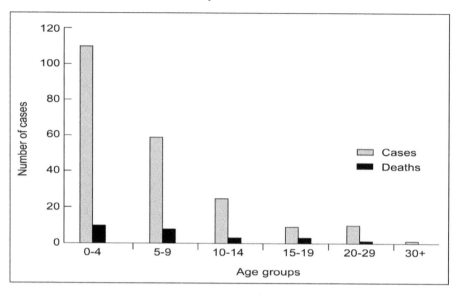

**Figure 5.4** Polio Cases and Deaths by Age Group, Sydney 1931-1932 Epidemic.

People were urged to get expert advice as soon as possible and not "to allow the chiropractor to interfere". Parents were urged to avoid taking children into crowds, to boil all their milk, protect food from flies and protect the back of the neck from the sun (*Sydney Morning Herald*, 8th January, 1932, p.8.). The Director General of Health, Dr Dick, urged people to give up the practice of kissing babies because of the risk of infection and that a notice *"Please don't kiss me"* should be hung on all cots (*Sydney Morning Herald*, 9th January 1932, p.11). Children up to the age of 12 were restricted from admission to all places of entertainment or places of assembly as well as being restricted from returning to school after the end of the summer holidays. Adults were advised not to mingle with young people. During the epidemic 139 cases were treated with convalescent serum prepared from the blood of infected people during the preceding two years. It remains doubtful whether or not such serum offered any degree of protection to infected cases.

## Polio in the late 1930s

The late 1930s saw a number of devastating outbreaks of polio and while the total number of cases did not approach the levels of the early 1950s, within the context of the population levels of the time, these outbreaks represent some of the most severe in Australian history. In particular, the Victorian and Tasmanian epidemics of 1937-38 stand as two of the most severe polio outbreaks ever recorded in the Western world. In the case of the Tasmanian epidemic, in the context of a total State population of only 240,000, the 1,006 cases of polio during the latter part of 1937 and early 1938, represented a devastating toll. Small towns like Burnie, Campbell Town and Queenstown as well as the urban areas of Hobart and Launceston, were particularly affected. All in all, probably more than 120 people died as a result of this epidemic, 81 during 1937-38 and the remainder in the ensuing years.

## The 1937-38 Epidemic in Victoria

Between July 1937 and the end of June 1938 Victoria suffered a major polio epidemic resulting in 2,096 cases, 1,300 of which occurred in the Melbourne Metropolitan area (Figure 5.5). In total 109 people died from polio during the epidemic. Victoria was ill-prepared for such an outbreak of polio. The disease appeared during a particularly cold and bleak winter month and reached a peak in early January 1938. Largely it affected young children under the age of nine years although more than 25 percent of cases were aged over 10 years (Figure 5.5). The epidemic commenced during July in the south-eastern Melbourne suburb of Ormond among children attending a local primary school and from there gradually spread to involve the whole metropolitan area of Melbourne. The epidemic reached a peak in November and then began a decline through the early months of 1938. During the epidemic the attack rate per 1,000 children aged less than 15 years varied across the city and suburbs, but it was the depressed inner city suburbs which fared the worst. As Figure 5.6 reveals, the attack rate varied from 11.6 cases per 1,000 for Port Melbourne, 9.2 for Melbourne City and 8.6 for South Melbourne to only 2.6 and 1.2 for the more affluent suburbs of Richmond and Prahan respectively.

During the epidemic a variety of measures were advanced to control the spread of the disease, but little was achieved. The Victorian Health Act provided for the isolation of Pre-School and school children and for the medical surveillance of adult contacts. Beyond this the Victorian Government was reluctant to go and rather than formally quarantine neighbourhoods and people, it appealed to the public for vigilance. In the City of Melbourne a coordinated approach to identify contacts and possible lines of infection was followed by health officers. Efforts were made to reconstruct the past history of cases and contacts so as to establish the possible history of infection and obtain a comprehensive list of contacts. Where it involved school contacts, schools were formally closed. A major problem confronting the authorities was that no one had established how the disease spread and what the medium of infection was. Following Canadian experience and the belief that the portal of entry for the virus was the olfactory nerves of the nose, nasal sprays were considered, but the technology of the time did not allow much progress.

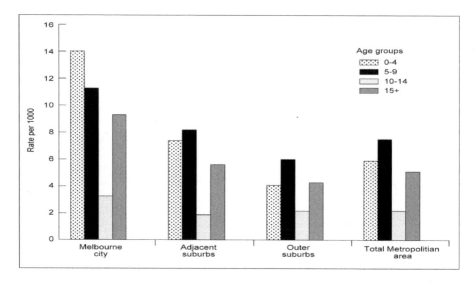

**Figure 5.5** Polio Cases by Age Group, Melbourne City and Suburbs During 1937-1938 Epidemic.

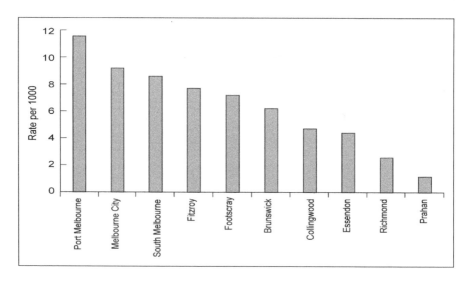

**Figure 5.6** Polio Attack Rate per 1,000 Population, Melbourne Metropolitan Area, 1937-1938 Epidemic.

**Table 5.4:** Age-Sex Structure of Polio Cases, Melbourne Metropolitan Area 1937-38

| Age Groups | Males | Females | Total |
|------------|-------|---------|-------|
| 0-4 | 250 | 165 | 4156 |
| 5-9 | 370 | 248 | 618 |
| 10-14 | 115 | 70 | 185 |
| 15-19 | 27 | 10 | 37 |
| 20+ | 27 | 18 | 45 |
| | | | |
| Total | 789 | 511 | 1300 |

Source: Data from Bull, 1939.

In fear of the epidemic spreading beyond Victoria, New South Wales requested that the Commonwealth formally declare a formal quarantine around Victoria in 1937, but the Commonwealth, mindful of failed attempts at such isolation in the past, refused to acquiesce. In retaliation, the New South Wales Government closed its southern border with Victoria to all children under the age of 16 years unless they had a current certificate of health attesting to the fact that they had had no contact with the disease in the preceding three weeks. New South Wales stationed 100 police at all border crossings to turn back children not in possession of a medical certificate. Special police were also deployed at railway stations, at the airport and at wharves in Sydney. South Australia followed suit, and over the next nine months tens of thousands of medical certificates were produced. New South Wales went one step further and passed a Public Health Amending Act which allowed the Government to formally proclaim any disease that might be passed from person to person as a communicable disease, and that any part of New South Wales or beyond could be subject to formal exclusion. Interestingly the New South Wales Act deliberately avoided using the term Quarantine so as to avoid direct conflict with the Commonwealth Government.

One of the most interesting features of the Melbourne epidemic was the fact that the disease largely affected children living in the city's most depressed inner city neighbourhoods where large families, overcrowding and socio-economic stress were most pronounced. This ran contrary to earlier studies of polio epidemics which placed considerable emphasis on the fact that the disease affected apparently healthy and well-cared for children from middle-class and more affluent neighbourhoods. Bull in her report on the epidemic in Melbourne suggested some possible reasons for this difference. In the first place, in Melbourne's inner-most suburbs most houses were very small terraces, cramped together with no backyards or gardens. By consequence, most children were forced to play on the streets where they closely mingled with neighbours. In such circumstances it proved impossible to isolate children effectively during the epidemic. In the second place, nearly all these inner city homes were unsewered and relied on the pan system (see Bull, 1939, p.21 and p.30). Throughout the epidemic there was considerable evidence of public anxiety and distress. People tended to boycott the homes or businesses of neighbours where a case was known to have occurred and avoid contact with people generally. Teenagers who had the misfortunate to be labelled as "contacts" were often barred from workplaces, or lost their jobs and saw their parents boycotted by workmates and friends. The return of a case from hospital in splints and crutches required considerable attention and placed a tremendous burden on all families.

## The Tasmanian Epidemic of 1937-38

The polio epidemic in Victoria had been raging for several months before the first case appeared in Tasmania. A seven year-old child from Inveresk near Launceston was hospitalized on the 5th of November 1937. Within a week, more cases were discovered in nearby Campbell Town and Launceston, and by December, the disease had spread to involve the south of the state. Peaking in December and January with over 200 cases in each month, the epidemic maintained a high incidence until May, with the last cases occurring in September (Figure 5.7). This particular outbreak stands out as the most severe in Australian history with 1,006 recorded cases and possibly 150 deaths. Within the context of a small, isolated state of little more than 240,000 people, these 1,006 cases represented an extraordinarily heavy toll and represented an overall rate of 42 cases per 10,000 population compared with the Victorian epidemic rate of only 13.5 per 10,000. Only the South Australian polio epidemic of 1950-51 comes anywhere near to this in severity, when 2,428 cases produced a rate of 34.2 cases of polio per 10,000 population. Like so many previous polio epidemics, the full impact of the Tasmanian outbreak fell on young children and teenagers. Eighty-three percent of all cases were children aged under 15 years, with 64 percent being aged less than nine years. Unlike the Victorian epidemic, the Tasmanian outbreak involved a slightly older population with 17 percent of all cases being aged over 15 years, including 6 percent over 25 years. With respect to the population aged under 9 years there was an extremely high infection rate of 142.7 polio cases per 10,000 population. As Table 5.5 indicates the rate for children under 15 years was not much lower at 121.5 per 10,000 population.

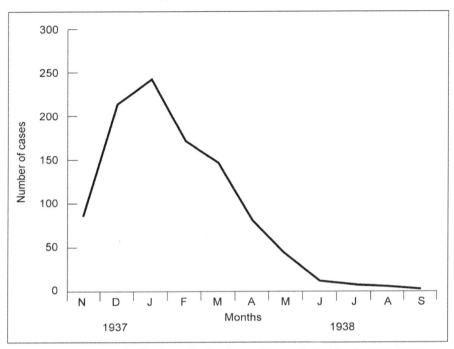

**Figure 5.7** Monthly Distribution of Polio Cases, Tasmania Epidemic 1937-1938.

| **Table 5.5:** Age Structure and Rate per 10,000. Tasmanian Polio Epidemic 1937 | | | |
|---|---|---|---|
| | | | |
| **Age Group (Years)** | **Polio Cases** | **Total Population** | **Rate per 10,000** |
| Under 9 | 644 | 45,134 | 142.69 |
| Under 15 | 833 | 68,590 | 121.45 |
| Under 20 | 903 | 91,191 | 99.02 |
| Under 25 | 946 | 111,561 | 84.8 |
| Under 30 | 974 | 129,082 | 75.5 |
| | | | |
| Source: 1933 Census and Killalea, 1995. | | | |

The epidemic was probably more severe than other polio epidemics to this point, insofar as, a large proportion of victims remained moderately or severely crippled for the rest of their lives. Almost one quarter of all people who caught the disease fell into this category. Of the 1,006 cases of polio, 81 died during 1937-38. By the early 1940s probably another 40 had died, bringing the total number of deaths to around 125, a case mortality rate of 12.4 percent. In total, more than one third of people who contracted polio during 1937-38 either died or had their lives shattered for ever.

The epidemic also had a distinctive geographic impact on the state. Generally, the two major urban areas of Hobart and Launceston shared the bulk of the cases, in total 41 percent. Launceston, a small regional town of some 33,000 inhabitants suffered more than Hobart with 200 cases. All in all, six municipalities accounted for more than 57 percent of all polio cases during 1937-38. The two major urban areas of Hobart and Launceston, the small coastal town of Burnie in the north, Kentish and Deloraine municipalities to the east of Launceston, and New Norfolk to the west of Hobart bore the brunt of the outbreak in 1937-38.

When the number of cases is plotted as a proportion of the population aged under 30 years of age (97 percent of all cases were aged under 30 years) a better view of the real impact of the epidemic emerges (Figure 5.8). The epidemic impacted heaviest on the young adult and child population inhabiting a belt of northern municipalities stretching from Waratah and Zeehan in the west, through Kentish and Deloraine to Launceston and Longford, and then to a group of north-eastern municipalities, including Ringarooma, Portland and Fingal. Four northern coastal areas were also involved: Burnie and Penguin towards the east, and Beaconsfield and George Town in the centre of the north coast. In the south of the state, three municipalities were particularly affected, namely Esperance in the far south and New Norfolk and Sorell in the south-east. Only two areas escaped the epidemic totally – King Island off the north-west coast, and Glamorgan a small isolated municipality in the west. The impact of the disease on small isolated Tasmanian communities can only be imagined. Burnie, a small north coast town of barely 6,000 persons, suffered more than 50 cases, many of them children. In a town of only 1,300 or so young children, the impact of this must have been profound.

More isolated parts of the state also suffered heavily. Portland municipality in the far north-east of the state, only had 16 polio cases, but in the context of a total population of little over 500 children aged under 15, this must have been a bitter blow. During the epidemic the Tasmanian authorities went to some lengths to try and contain the disease and stop it from spreading. The situation that applied in and around the town of Launceston sums up the official measures advanced. In Launceston the movement of children was restricted and any child who had the misfortunate to be in the same school class as someone who caught polio was placed in isolation for 21 days. Local schools were often closed. In early April, *The Mercury* announced new restrictions. All children aged under 17 years were forbidden to leave Launceston or Campbelltown without a medical statement to the effect that they were free of infection and had had no contact with anyone thought to have polio (see *The Mercury*, 13 April, 1937, p.9). They were also banned from attending any church, Sunday school or any place of recreation or sport. Local fairs and celebrations were all cancelled and people discouraged from taking children on visits or trips outside the towns. Fear of infection was widespread and all pervading. Children thought to be infected or to have attended the same school as someone who was were given a wide berth and their parents shunned. People also were uncomfortable in handling money, speaking on the telephone or letting their children play outside.

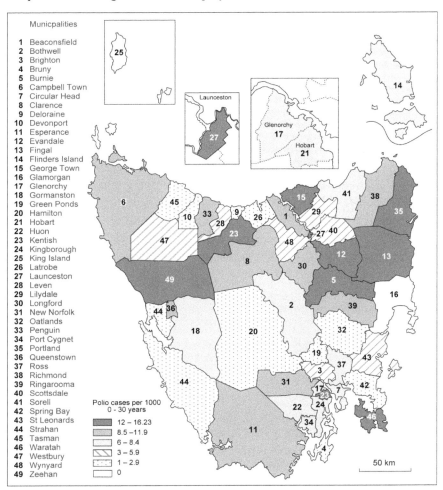

**Figure 5.8** Geographical Distribution of Polio Cases per 1,000 Aged 0-30 Years, Tasmania Epidemic 1937-1938.

## The Causes of Polio

Even though the polio virus had been identified in the first decade of the 20th century, the causes of the disease and its means of transmission remained an area of considerable debate for almost 50 years. Given that most doctors and public health experts had come to associate infectious disease with the poor, the deprived, and those living in squalid and unsanitary urban conditions, the fact that many polio patients were apparently healthy, strong and well-nourished children, from middle class backgrounds, raised many questions. For some reason polio seemed to select the clean, well fed and suburban child. Draper, an American physician, whose 1917 text on polio was widely circulated in Australasia, adopted a very physiographic approach by arguing that certain physical types were more susceptible to the disease. Draper observed that, "the type of child which seems to be most susceptible to the disease is the large well grown plump individual, who has certain definite characteristics of face and jaws, is broad browed, and broad and round of face." (Drew, 1933, p.27). Draper went further. He noticed "that in 50-60 percent of all cases at Locust Valley, all the central incisor teeth of the upper jaw were separated by a cleft of varying width." (Drew, 1933, p.27). Such views were widely canvassed in Australia during the 1920s and 1930s.

The manner in which the virus entered and spread within the body was also an area that remained unresolved until the 1950s. Many medical experts argued strongly that the micro-organism travelled through the nerves directly after entering the body and hence polio was primarily a neurological disease. This view tended to dominate medical thinking and influence treatment at least until 1950 even though challenged by Elizabeth Kenny and her supporters in the 1940s. They argued vociferously, that polio was a muscle disease and not a nerve disease and hence required a different approach by way of treatment. By then, however, a new model of transmission had become accepted. Polio was seen to enter the body through the mouth and travel to the intestines via the blood and only rarely did the virus affect the nervous system. In many ways, the rise of polio among affluent middle class communities reflected advances in public health and sanitation and the pursuit of cleanliness that characterized the first few decades of the 20th century. The virus, widespread and largely silent up to this point, only became a problem when dirt, poverty and urban crowding became less prevalent. In the crowded, unsanitary conditions of 19th century cities, most children were exposed to the virus and probably immune to further attacks by the age of three. As prosperity, cleanliness and suburban development spread so too did polio. Probably critical in all of this were advances in waste disposal, public sanitation and the reticulation of pure water and unadulterated food, all of which helped break the chain of gastrointestinal infection.

While the medical authorities had their view on what caused polio, the means of transmission of the virus remained elusive. Many doctors thought the virus was transmitted directly from person to person by some unknown mechanism, but most believed that the route was via the respiratory system. Consequently, people were advised to avoid crowds, playgrounds, cinemas and libraries or church services or anywhere where groups of people assembled. Competitive sports and rallies for young people were cancelled. Others argued the possibility of it being transmitted by water. People were urged to boil all drinking water, avoid sharing cups or drinking utensils and to keep away from swimming pools. Beer drinkers were urged to realize the danger of polio lurking in the unwashed glass. For many, insects and animals remained an obvious link with the disease. Fleas, mosquitoes and flies were all put forward as possible vectors possibly spreading the disease from rubbish and horse manure or possibly from human faeces.

People were urged to protect all food from flies. Some argued that domestic pets spread the disease with the result that many people abandoned or killed their cats and dogs. Others saw the wind as the agent of transmission. Milk also came under suspicion and the presence of formalin commonly used as a preservative in milk led to a number of studies of the effects of formalin on guinea pigs. The occurrence of polio epidemics during the spring and summer inevitably led some to claim that exposure to sunlight was linked to the disease. The wearing of hats with neck flaps was urged by health authorities until the late 1940s. One writer claimed that epidemics usually occurred within three months of the annual dog registration. In Victoria the registration fees were highest for Alsatian dogs and some claimed that the reason lay in the fact that such dogs were about the height of the noses of 5-10 year-old children, among whom the incidence of polio was very high. In 1950 others claimed that polio was somehow linked to the whooping cough/diphtheria inoculations of young children.

## The Cult of "Straightness" and the Avoidance of Crippling Deformity

Fear of polio was undoubtedly increased by the lack of medical knowledge about the aetiology of the disease and the failure of doctors to come up with an effective means of predicting epidemics or providing treatment. Polio had in fact been extensively researched in America from the first decade of the 20th century and the disease was conclusively established as an infection as early as 1909. Yet, until the 1950s the only weapons that the medical community had to combat the disease were the time-honoured ones of public health, quarantine, isolation, hospitalization, cleanliness and appeals for calm.

With respect to actual treatment, the medical profession fell back on the procedure of immobilization, rest and restraint. The procedure in place at the Children's Hospital in Brisbane in 1932 sums up the approach. Parents and visitors were actively prevented from seeing their children so as to avoid any form of stimulation. Once the initial fever and acute phase of the disease had passed, treatment focused on preventing deformity as a result of weakened or damaged muscles. Complete muscular rest was advocated by immobilising the patient's trunk and limbs by using plaster casts and rigorous splinting. Massage was actively discouraged. Such treatment was supposed to allow muscles to avoid being damaged so that they might be reactivated at a later date. Among other things such a treatment regime undoubtedly served the purpose of keeping young children firmly under control while theoretically allowing damaged limbs to be kept straight so as to avoid long-term crippling deformity. Until there was evidence of muscle recovery and/or loss of pain, immobilization and total bed rest were the orders of the day. In some cases sufferers remained immobilized for six months or more. Unfortunately, the method rested more on theory than clinical testing and frequently failed. When muscle weakness and soreness had passed, treatment centred on physical therapy designed to reactivate damaged muscles. In some cases, physicians recommended orthopaedic surgery to help correct deformed limbs or joints. In the United States during the 1916 epidemic and over the following 14 years, a number of polio researchers/practitioners experimented with injections of serum derived from the tissue of infected patients. Early work seemed to indicate some degree of success in preventing or reducing paralysis particularly if the serum was delivered in the pre-paralytic stage, however, later trials tended not to confirm this, and few studies found any statistical evidence of better results after serum treatment. By the 1930s the use of serum injections was largely abandoned as being largely ineffective. In Australia, the serum method remained the only preventative treatment available. Dr Jean Macnamarra of the Royal Children's Hospital in Melbourne remained the most vocal advocate of serum treatment in the early 1930s, although even she was forced ultimately to accept that coordinated after-care was critical to recovery. During the 1931-32 epidemic, serum treatment produced from the blood of infected patients was widely canvassed via the medium of the Infantile Paralysis Committee of New South Wales formed by Sir Charles Clubbe a year or two earlier. Serum depots were established in many country centres throughout New South Wales and of the 214 polio patients treated in Sydney during the epidemic, 139 had serum administered some in the pre-paralytic stage and some after the signs of paralysis had appeared. While no proper control study was ever mounted, the results suggest that for those administered serum before the onset of paralysis, the chance of the disease progressing to paralysis was low. Critically, however, this may have been because of the mildness of the infection and/or because in many such cases the disease did not always progress to full paralysis. For those administered serum after the onset of paralysis the treatment seemed to have had little effect.

A critical plank of treatment throughout the period was early diagnosis followed by appropriate treatment. The only problem was that it was not easy to diagnose polio in its early stages as the disease symptoms tended to be indistinguishable from flu. Only when actual paralysis appeared was diagnosis possible. Macnamarra had been closely involved in research and the treatment of polio cases from the early 1930s. She advocated a mix of orthodox medical treatment followed by after-care treatment involving massage, but always under the supervision of trained medical practitioners. She remained a firm opponent of the Kenny method and regularly advanced her views publically and through the local press. Through the 1940s, Kenny's methods continued to gain acceptance, until by the 1950s they were largely incorporated into mainstream physiotherapy.

## Changing Age Incidence

One of most interesting aspects of the history of polio in Australia was the changing susceptibility of age groups. Prior to the 1930s most polio cases occurred in infants under five years of age except in small isolated communities where older children were often affected. In the Queensland outbreak of 1904 for example, almost 90 percent of cases were aged less than five years and even by 1931-32 three quarters of all cases were young infants. By the late 1940s the age incidence of the disease had shifted substantially and the proportion of infants had fallen below 25 percent. Most significantly, polio had shifted from being primarily a disease of very young children to one affecting adolescents and young adults. In the 1947-48 South Australian epidemic for example, 43.7 percent of all cases were aged over 15 years, with an additional 20 percent aged between 10-14 years. This indicates a real change in the behaviour of the disease over the first 40 or so years of the century. Burnet pointed out in 1940 that the age incidence of polio in North America seemed to vary between rural and urban communities with the disease affecting higher age groups in the former. Some evidence for this is found in the results of the 1937-38 epidemic in New South Wales. In that epidemic almost 22 percent of cases in rural New South Wales were aged over 15 years, compared with about 10 percent of metropolitan Sydney cases (Helms, 1941, p.470). By contrast, three quarters of all Sydney cases were aged less than nine years compared to only 46 percent of rural cases. Figure 5.9 graphically displays the changing age incidence in New South Wales between 1915 and 1937-38 with data from the South Australian epidemic of 1947-48. The shift in age incidence away from infants is dramatic, as is the increase among older children and adults.

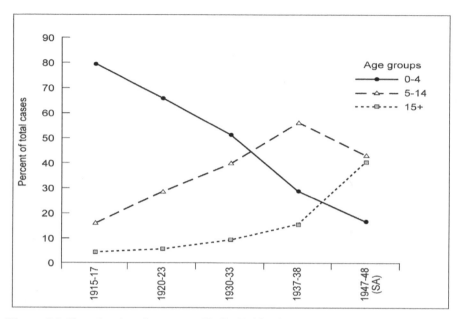

**Figure 5.9** Changing Age Structure of Polio Epidemics 1915-1948.

## Polio After 1949

In the years after 1948 Australia suffered a series of major outbreaks of polio. Whereas up until 1949 major epidemics had developed a temporal spacing of between four and six years, between 1949 and 1956 polio became a regular annual event, with major epidemics in Victoria in 1949, New South Wales and South Australia in 1950-51, Tasmania in 1951-53, and New South Wales and Victoria in 1953-54. The years 1950-51 were particularly severe when 6,411 cases were officially notified including 4,779 in New South Wales and South Australia alone. By 1949 medical views and opinions about the origins and mechanisms of spread of the disease had changed very little from those that prevailed during the 1930s. In 1949-50, scientists and the medical profession thought it highly significant that polio epidemics usually occurred during the summer months when flies were numerous and excreta often exposed to heat and humidity (See *Sydney Morning Herald*, 23 December, 1949, p.2). They also suggested that the infection might be spread via milk products and that children who had recently had their tonsils removed were more susceptible to infection. In 1949-50 when new epidemics threatened, first in Victoria and then in New South Wales and South Australia, no time was lost in isolating cases and contacts, closing schools, draining swimming pools and prohibiting children moving from their homes. Such was the public's fear of infection that anyone seen to create a risk was pursued by the law with vigour such as the three or four Sanitary Carriers in Sydney's Sutherland Shire who were prosecuted and fined for dumping sanitary pans in the bush. The entire Shire's Sanitary Carriers went on strike in protest, but in the words of the district's Chief Health officer, "such workers were holding the community to ransom and spreading polio through the community" (*Sydney Morning Herald*, 18 February, 1950, p.4). Polio continued to produce fear and terror throughout the early 1950s. In 1951, 1,562 cases occurred in New South Wales as well as 40 deaths and over the next five years polio continued its assault on the Australian population.

For many the battle against polio was won in the years after 1956 with the advent of the Salk and Sabin anti-viral treatment. In Australia a major vaccination program commenced during the latter part of 1956 and continued in subsequent years. Within a few years (Plates 5.2, 5.3 and 5.4) polio had virtually disappeared from Australia. While the defeat of polio represents a triumph for medical science almost on a par with that achieved in the defeat of smallpox, one of the more disturbing trends of recent years has been the re-emergence of a late or post-polio syndrome. Some believe that this is simply a second stage of polio infection. Only people previously infected by the virus are threatened and it is likely that thousands of Australians could be at risk. The most commonly reported symptoms include, fatigue, joint and muscle pain, sleeping, breathing and swallowing difficulties and increased sensitivity to temperature change. To this point, the causes of the syndrome remain unknown. Equally disturbing is the re-emergence of polio in some parts of the developing world such as Pakistan and Somalia with the possibility of countries importing wild polio virus from such countries. Like all infectious diseases with polio the pendulum remains finely balanced.

# PLATES

**Plate 1.1:** S.S. Zealandia, 1913. Photogrpah by Henry Allport. With thanks to the State Library of Tasmania.

**Plate 1.2:** Crew of S.S. Zealandia undergoing quarantine inspection at Freemantle after leaving Sydney in 1913. Crew includes the 3rd class steward responsible for the smallpox outbreak in New South Wales. Source: Image PRG 280/1/16/86. Courtesy of the State Library of South Australia.

**Plate 1.3:** Official newspaper announcements re quarantine July 1913.
Source: *The Daily Mail*, 5th & 7th July 1913, page 13 and page 9.

# VIGILANT.

## FIGHTING SMALLPOX

## CAMPAIGN OF ACTIVITY.

### FEDERAL PROCLAMATION.

### OPERATES FROM TO-DAY.

### INTER-STATE PRECAUTIONS.

### OVER 15,000 VACCINATIONS IN SYDNEY.

The Plague once met a Pilgrim, who said to him, "Where are you going?"
The Plague replied, "I am going to Bagdad to kill 5000 people."
The Pilgrim some time later met the Plague returning, and said to him, "Hello, I thought you said you were only going to kill 5000 people. You killed 50,000."
"No," retorted the Plague, "I killed but 5000. The others died of fright!"
So runs an ancient fable. In these days of alarums and excursions it seems applicable. Sydney is just now harboring an unwelcome and uninvited plague, whose name is Smallpox. He came stealthily, as a thief in the night, sapping the vitality of man. But, as yet, he has not shown us his worst side; he has been merciful, and, though much sickness has followed in his train, his victims live. His pathway has not been strewn with roses, and, instead of being showered with sweet essences, he has been smothered with evil-smelling concoctions, and treated to such rough usage that he may soon be gone. Meantime, though it be wise to be cautious, and to pay heed to the advice of the physician, there is no need for people to emulate the crowded hordes of old Bagdad and die of fright.

#### THE PATIENTS.

There are now 38 patients in hospital at North Head, none of whom are seriously ill. In addition, 67 convalescents and contacts are detained at the station, making a total of 105, all told, in actual quarantine. The sum total of the work of the Health Department on Saturday and Sunday, therefore, is that the population at the Quarantine Station has been increased by 48, 17 of which number represent new cases.

"It must not be assumed that these are actually new cases of smallpox," said the Secretary of the Health Department yesterday. "They are for the most part patients who have been ill for some little time, but whose predicament

# QUARANTINED.

## SYDNEY UNDER HEALTH LAW.

## DECLARED INFECTED.

### WITHIN 15 MILES RADIUS.

### STRINGENT FEDERAL REGULATIONS.

### INTER-STATE TRAFFIC UNDER SURVEILLANCE.

### RUSH FOR VACCINATION.

The Federal authorities dropped a bombshell into New South Wales last night. Sydney, within an area of 15 miles from the General Post-office, has been declared a quarantine area.
This step was taken by Executive authority yesterday, under the provisions of the Federal Quarantine Act, upon the recommendation of the Director of Quarantine, Dr. Cumpston, who was in Sydney this week in connection with the outbreak of smallpox now being handled by the State Department of Public Health.
The Federal Executive at the same time passed a series of regulations prescribing the precautions which are to be taken in regard to the ingress or egress from the quarantined area whenever such action may be found necessary. These prohibit, among other things, any person who has not been successfully vaccinated within the last five years from leaving the infected area for the purpose of journeying to another State. Each person so journeying from the proclaimed area will be under quarantine surveillance, and will require to report himself. The penalty for non-observance of the regulation is £50.
Although Sydney was in quarantine to all intents and purposes as from 6.30 o'clock last evening, the drastic regulations will not to-day be applied to passengers by steamers or

Plates

**Plate 1.4:** Quarantine Station at North Head, Sydney. Source: Peter Curson.

**Plate 1.5:** North Head Sydney Quarantine Station buildings near wharf. Source: The Sydney Mail, 31st March 1900.

**Plate 1.6:** 28-year old male smallpox case admitted to Quarantine Station, in 10th day of efflorescence. Source: Robertson, 1914, No. 12.

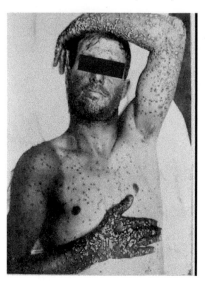

**Plate 2.1:** "X" Disease Press release 1918. Source: Daily Telegraph, 12th February 1918, page 4.

### CONCERNING "X."

#### A NEW COMPLAINT.

#### SIMILAR TO MENINGITIS.

The letter "X" is the only name that has so far been given to a new disease which has occurred in the north-west of New South Wales, and which the Board of Health is investigating.

"X" it has been called until experiment and research have sufficiently established its nature to enable it to be more appropriately indicated.

An officer in the Health Department said yesterday that while the disease was new in the sense that so far as medical records go it has not been discovered in other countries, yet it was known to exist here some months ago. He added that there was not the slightest cause for alarm. The number of cases was small—about half the number of those of meningitis—and the board was taking every precaution against its spreading, as well as experimenting thoroughly to discover the best best methods of treating patients.

The disease, in its symptoms, closely resembles cerebro-spinal meningitis, though it differs pathologically. Neither is it as serious in its after-effects as infantile paralysis. So far the board has not had the legal power to deal with contacts as with meningitis, as "X" is not listed as a notifiable disease. That discrepancy will probably be rectified in the near future. Meantime it will have to be named. "X" has aroused considerable interest in medical circles, and a recent issue of the "Medical Journal of New South Wales" contained an interesting, if highly technical, article on the new disease.

So far this year 19 cases of meningitis have been reported. This is not an unusually large number. The Health Department records show that an excess of that total was notified during the corresponding periods of last year and 1916.

Nor can it be said that meningitis is especially prevalent in any particular district, as the cases came from widely scattered towns in all parts of the State. Still, the Health Department officers claim to be taking no risks of the disease assuming serious proportions when the colder weather comes on. Rigorous steps are being taken to prevent its spread.

Plates

**Plate 3.1:** "Breaking & Entering", James Case's cartoon of the struggle between the Acting Australian Prime Minister William Watt and the Queensland Government over Queensland's decision to unilaterally close its borders and institute formal quarantine in 1919. Courtesy of the National Archives of Australia.

BREAKING AND ENTERING.

**Plate 3.2:** Riley Street Influenza Depot, Sydney, nurses and staff. Source: Image dl_13498. Courtesy State Library of New South Wales.

**Plate 3.3:** Hospital beds in Great Hall, Melbourne Exhibition Building during the influenza pandemic of 1919. Source: Image MM103429, Courtesy of the Museum of Victoria.

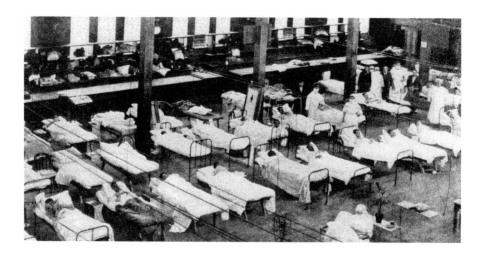

Plates

**Plate 3.4:** Influenza inoculation at Hyde Park Depot and crowd at Inoculation Depot. Source: Sydney Mail, 5th February 1919, page 18.

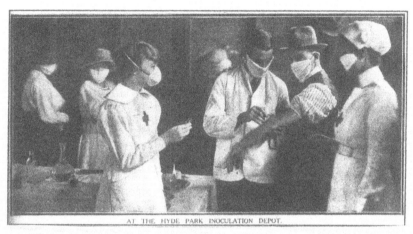

AT THE HYDE PARK INOCULATION DEPOT.

THE CROWD AT ONE OF THE CITY INOCULATION DEPOTS EARLY IN THE WEEK.

**Plate 3.5:** Influenza Quarantine Camp, Jubilee Oval, Adelaide, 1919. Source: Photograph PRG 280/1/15/432. Courtesy of the State Library of South Australia.

**Plate 3.6:** Chamberlain's Cough Remedy. Source: The Bulletin, February 1919.

Plates

**Plate 4.1:** Dengue Mosquito, *Aedes Aegypti*. Source: ID9261. Courtesy CDC Public Health Image Library & F.H. Collins.

**Plate 4.2:** ASPRO and DENGUE advertisement, 1926. Source: Maryborough Chronicle, ide Bay and Burnett Advertiser, 24th March 1926, page 3.

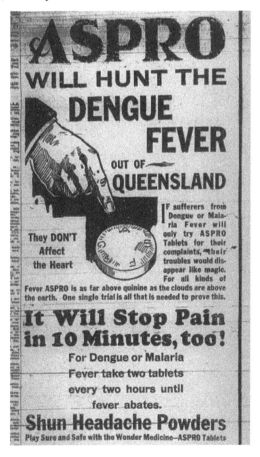

**Plate 4.3:** FLY-TOX advertisement, 1926. Source: The Brisbane Courier, 1st April 1926, page 12.

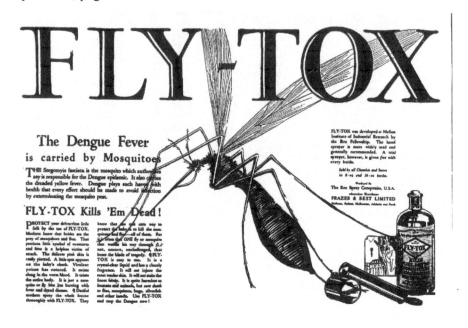

**Plate 4.4:** Australian Dengue fever poster, 1940s. Source: Image MO742/1. Courtesy of the National Archives of Australia.

**Plate 5.1:** Young polio child on crutches at Margaret Reid Hospital, New South Wales Society for Crippled Children, St. Ives, Sydney. Source: Image d_707311. Courtesy of the State Library of New South Wales.

**Plate 5.2:** Vaccination against polio at Randwick Girls School, Sydney. Source: Image d2_07705. Courtesy of the State Library of New South Wales.

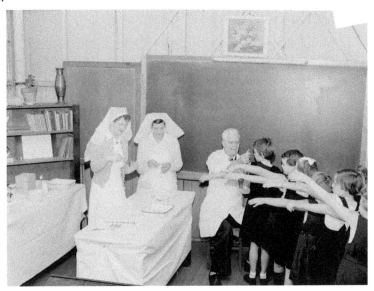

**Plate 5.3:** Iron Lung, Royal North Shore Hospital, Sydney. Source: Image d_211851. Courtesy of the State Library of New South Wales.

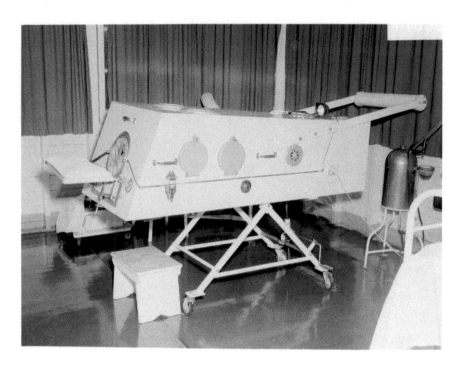

**Plate 5.4:** Sister Elizabeth Kenny, pioneer of alternative Polio treatment. Source: Image hood_26494. Courtesy of the State Library of New South Wales.

Plates

**Plate 6.1:** Australian HIV/AIDS poster. Source: Image L0052679. Courtesy of the Welcome Library London and the Australian National Council on AIDS.

**Plate 7.1:** "PLAGUE FEAR Sars, superbugs and the coming winter," The New Zealand Listener, May 10-16, 2003, cover page. Courtesy of the New Zealand Listener/Bauer Media.

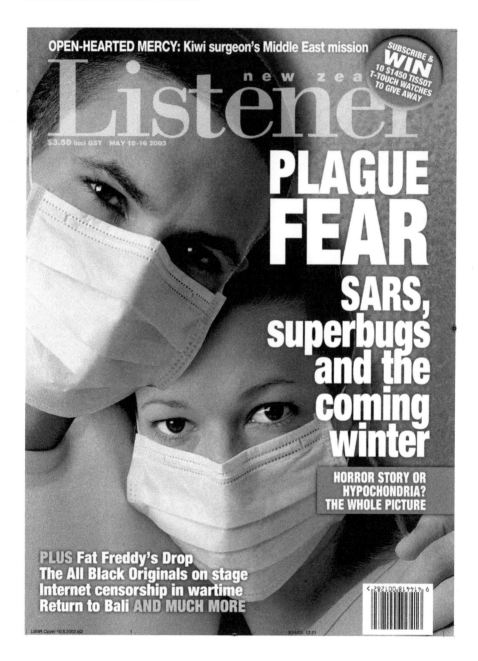

# CHAPTER 6

# Spreading Dis-Ease – HIV/AIDS

## The Origins of HIV/AIDS

We are now entering the fourth decade of what may eventually turn out to be the most devastating infectious disease in history: HIV/AIDS. Since the early 1980s some 35 million people around the world have died from HIV/AIDS related illnesses and today there are more than 36 million people infected with the HIV virus. HIV/AIDS is not one but three inter-twined epidemics. The first is an epidemic of HIV infection. The second inexorably linked to the first but with a time lag of several years, is an epidemic of the disease AIDS. Finally, there is a third epidemic of psycho-social reaction manifesting in stigma, rejection, discrimination, fear and panic.

The human immunodeficiency virus (HIV) is a highly contagious virus that can lead to the development of acquired immunodeficiency syndrome (AIDS). While the two are often referred to as HIV/AIDS, they are not synonymous. AIDS was first recognised in 1981, after doctors began noticing clusters of unexplainable illnesses, and was linked to the HIV virus shortly after. The history of HIV/AIDS is a complex one and one that was poorly understood until relatively recently. There is little doubt that the virus is primarily a zoonosis or animal disease that most probably circulated among its primary host – chimpanzees and monkeys in parts of central and western Africa, possibly for centuries. It was only when colonialism disrupted the natural environment via the medium of indentured and forced labour to exploit the rubber and ivory trade allied to local efforts to vaccinate people against sleeping sickness by reusing the same syringes and needles that the virus made the jump to humans. Possibly the virus had circulated amongst humans in what was formerly the German Cameroons, the French and Belgian Congo and Portuguese Angola for much of the late 19th and early 20th centuries without attracting any notice (see Keys, 2012, pp.16-18). By the first few decades of the 20th century in response to a boom in the cotton, palm oil and copper trade in parts of Central Africa, the Belgian authorities encouraged the migration of young male workers as labourers to work on the many development projects in the Belgian Congo. The gender imbalance that resulted from this migration led to a rise in prostitution and an increase in sexually transmitted diseases. The government's reaction was to institute a major vaccination program again relying on the reuse of needles and syringes. There is little doubt now that this facilitated the spread of HIV/AIDS. The final act in this tragedy occurred many years later, when following the bloodshed and mayhem following independence, UNESCO resolved to send thousands of teachers and other professionals to the Congo, many from Haiti. At least one Haitian teacher contracted HIV/AIDS and returned home in the late 1960s and unknowingly became the medium whereby HIV/AIDS was introduced to America. Haiti at this time was a mecca for sex tours and male HIV spread out of Africa via Haiti to the United States, where is it thought to have arrived in just one person as early as the late 1960s (*Science Daily* 2007). Once it reached the United States, it then eventually spread to Europe, Australia and New Zealand. From the mid-1970s to the early-1980s, HIV/AIDS became a serious problem, particularly among the male homosexual community, with over 50 percent of homosexual men in some urban areas directly affected (Sigma/Swiss Re, 1988, p.5). This ultimately gave birth to the label the "Gay Epidemic" and HIV/AIDS became negatively associated with a number of sectors of society, including homosexuals, haemophiliacs, Haitians, and heroin addicts.

## The Disease

AIDS is an auto-immune deficiency syndrome caused by the human immunodeficiency virus HIV (Lamptey, et.al, 2008, p.4). The HIV virus weakens the immune system by infecting and destroying white blood cells critical to the normal functioning of the immune system, leaving the infected person increasingly susceptible to numerous opportunistic infections and illnesses. The Australian National Council on AIDS defined the four stages of infection that follow exposure to HIV. Stage one, known as the 'primary infection' stage, develops within a few weeks of exposure and can last up to a 14 days. This stage is often characterised by fever, sore throat, lethargy, headaches, and swollen lymph nodes. Approximately 70 percent of infected persons experience this initial stage. Stage Two, 'early infection', is a period of 'viral latency', which can last from a few months to a number of years during which time infected persons are largely asymptomatic, although they may experience swollen lymph nodes. Stage Three, the 'middle infection' phase, is characterised by 'viral reactivation', with infected persons becoming increasingly susceptible to minor infections and conditions. The fourth and final stage is known as 'severe HIV disease'. It is during this final stage that AIDS as a disease emerges with pulmonary, gastrointestinal and neurological issues become common, as well as viral induced cancers, including Kaposi sarcoma and Non-Hodgkin's lymphoma (Australian National Council on AIDS, 1990).

The four stages of HIV/AIDS infection develop along with the depletion of T4 cells, which occur in the immune system. A healthy individual has about 1000 T4 cells per cubic millimetre of blood. However, in someone infected with HIV, the T4 cell count begins to drop significantly. When an infected persons T4 cell count reaches 400 – 800 cells per cubic millimetres of blood, the first telltale signs of infection start to appear. This can include skin and mucus membrane infections, including thrush, as well as diarrhoea, weight loss, fevers, night sweats, and persistent coughing. When the T4 cell count falls below 200 cells per cubic millimetres of blood, the individual can be defined as having AIDS with serious opportunistic infections developing, including pneumocystis pneumonia, cryptococcal meningitis, and toxoplasmosis. It is these opportunistic infections which are the most debilitating for HIV/AIDS sufferers, leading to 90 percent of AIDS-related deaths (Sherman, 2007, p.178). The time between contracting HIV and developing AIDS varies between individuals. Some infected persons show symptoms within 12 months, while others are asymptomatic for up to 10 years.

The HIV virus is found in the secretions and body fluids of infected individuals. This includes semen, vaginal secretions, blood, and breast milk. A tear in the skin or mucous membrane is required for the infected fluid to cause infection. As well as being sexually transmitted, infection can also result from the reuse of unsterile needles, from transplants of infected organs, transfusions of infected blood, and drinking infected breast milk. It is estimated that there are 34 million people around the world living with HIV (World Health Organisation, 2012), with 14,000 new infections occurring each day (Sherman 2007, p. 186).

Despite a significant effort by the scientific community over the last 30 years, there still remains no cure for HIV/AIDS. While there are antiretroviral (ART) drugs available that can suppress the HIV virus and slow the progression of the disease, the HIV virus can quickly adapt to evade any drug. Combination antiretroviral therapy, which commonly involves taking three drugs at one time, makes it more difficult for the virus to adapt. An Australian survey of people living with HIV, found that 79.6 percent were currently using ART, and 85 percent had used the drugs at some time in the past (Forbes, 2011, p. 32).

Post-exposure prophylaxis (PEP) is also available to persons who may have come into contact with HIV immediately following exposure. In the late 1980s, health care workers who were exposed to HIV were often given a course of ART, specifically the drug anti-viral zidovudine (AZT), to prevent sero-conversion. This practice has been extended to become available to any persons who may have come into contact with HIV. Pre-exposure prophylaxis (PrEP) has also been tested as a strategy to prevent HIV infection before exposure occurs.

ART treatments are useful in delaying the onset of the HIV virus, and improving the quality of life for those affected by HIV. However, the drugs are of little use if not taken correctly, requiring a certain level of education, knowledge and commitment on the part of the infected person. Critically, drug treatments are also expensive, making them less accessible to HIV-infected persons in the developing world, where a significant proportion of HIV cases are concentrated.

## HIV/AIDS in Australia

The first cases of HIV/AIDS were diagnosed in Australia in 1982-83. It is likely that HIV entered Sydney's homosexual community from the United States around the year 1980. It is difficult to gauge the extent of the HIV/AIDS epidemic in Australia in the 1980s. Some estimates place the HIV infection rate among Sydney's homosexual community at 40 percent by 1984 (Crofts, 1992, p. 14). In September 1986, the *National Times on Sunday* reported that 9,000 of Sydney's 250,000 homosexuals were known to have HIV, with a further 50,000 suspected to have contracted the virus (Crisp, 1986, p. 25). These figures seem somewhat exaggerated. *The Australian* newspaper reported in July 1985 that 96 AIDS cases had been confirmed in Australia, 41 of who had died (McNicoll, 1985, p.13). However, the *National Times on Sunday* reported just over a year later that 249 deaths had occurred across the country (Crisp, 1986, p.25). Other official reports suggest that by the end of 1987, 7,116 people had been diagnosed with HIV across Australia, and 797 with AIDS, with the majority of cases being males (AVERT, 2010). In 2012 the Kirby Institute stated that by the end of 2011 there had been 31,645 cases of HIV infection diagnosed in Australia and that an estimated 24,731 people were living with the HIV infection.

As Figure 6.1 indicates the number of new HIV diagnoses in Australia peaked in 1987, and then steadily declined until 1999, when 718 individuals were diagnosed. Since 1999, however, the annual number of diagnoses has increased each year. The 2012 Annual Surveillance Report released by the Kirby Institute puts the figure for new HIV diagnoses in 2011 at 1,137, an 8.2 percent increase on 2010. (The Kirby Institute, 2012, p.7). Both the rates of newly diagnosed and newly acquired HIV infection are dominated by male to male sexual contact – 63 percent and 83 percent respectively from 2006 – 2010. Heterosexual contact accounted for 25 percent and 10 percent of newly diagnosed and newly acquired HIV infections respectively, with minimal diagnoses due to injecting drug use and other/undetermined causes (Figure 6.2). People born in Australia made up the majority of newly diagnosed cases between 2006 and 2010 while the proportion of people diagnosed with HIV from Sub-Saharan Africa increased substantially (The Kirby Institute, 2011, p.11). When compared with other similarly developed countries, the rate of HIV diagnoses in Australia is much lower with 115 diagnoses per 100,000 people compared with a rate of 150 per 100,000 people in the United Kingdom and 456 per 100,000 people in the United States (The Kirby Institute, 2012, p.11).

By March 1992, 3,096 people had been diagnosed with AIDS in Australia equating to 19.4 cases per 100,000 people. The epidemic remained largely concentrated among men, with a ratio of 32:1 male to female cases (Crofts, 1992, p.14). The annual number of AIDS diagnoses peaked in 1994 at 953 cases. AIDS diagnoses declined rapidly to 216 in 1999, and have remained relatively stable since (Forbes, 2011, p.15). By the end of 2009, 10,446 AIDS cases had been diagnosed in Australia, and 6,776 AIDS-related deaths had occurred (Forbes, 2011, p.15).Rates of HIV are beginning to increase once again in Australia. This can largely be attributed to males engaging in unsafe sexual behaviour.

A number of studies have found that group sex is common among homosexual men and men who have sex with other men in Australia (Prestage et al., 2010), (Fig.6.2). A 2012 study found that one third of respondents reported having sex with more than 10 partners in the six months prior to their diagnosis, and that three-fifths had unprotected anal intercourse with a casual partner in the six months prior to their diagnosis (Down, et al., 2012, p.6). Interestingly when asked about perceptions of personal risk during the event that may have led to their diagnosis, one third reported that they did not even think about it, one half thought the risk was low or very low, and three quarters did not do anything to reduce the risk. A mere one in ten believed they were at high risk of infection (Down et al., 2012, p.38). The increase in risky behaviour can be attributed mainly to the increased well-being of HIV positive people, particularly as a result of ART. This has lead to a somewhat blasé attitude towards HIV transmission (Holt et al., 2012, p.1).

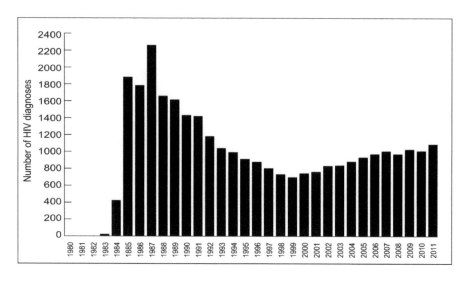

**Figure 6.1** HIV Diagnoses in Australia, 1983-2011.

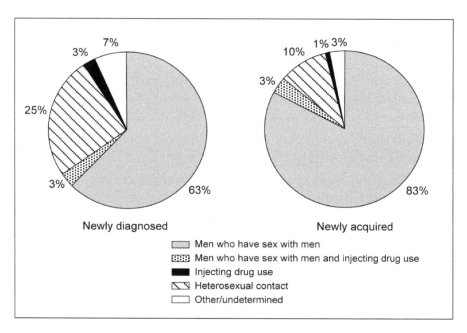

**Figure 6.2** Exposure Route to HIV/AIDS in Australia.

## Blood Transfusions

The first reported cases of HIV as a result of contact with infected blood occurred in 1982, when three haemophiliacs developed HIV following blood transfusions. In May 1983, homosexuals were banned from donating blood, and in 1984, a questionnaire related to 'at risk' behaviour was introduced along with donor declaration forms. These were legal documents with possible jail terms or fines for making false declarations. Since the mid-1980s, there has been no known transmission of HIV through infected blood or blood products. A nationwide publicity campaign in 1988 encouraged the 200,000 recipients of blood transfusions between 1980 and 1985 to come forward for testing. Of the 6,000 who presented, only 16 were found to be HIV positive (Wylie, 1992, p.72). The Kirby Institute's 2012 report states that levels of HIV infection in blood donors have fallen below 1 per 100,000 donations since 1985 (The Kirby Institute, 2012, p.26).

## IUDS

Australia has managed to avoid what is known as the "second wave" of the HIV/ AIDS epidemic, which involves injecting drug users (IDUs). In 1992, there were an estimated 30–50,000 regular IDUs in Australia, and approximately 60,000 occasional users (Wodak, 1992, p.28). The low rate of HIV amongst Australian IDUs can be attributed to very successful national needle and syringe programs (NSPs). From 2002 until 2011, the Kirby Institute reported that IDUs made up a mere six percent of HIV diagnoses, and over half of these were also men who had sex with men (The Kirby Institute, 2012, p.22).

## Indigenous Population

The rate of HIV diagnoses amongst the Aboriginal and Torres Strait Islander populations in Australian is similar to that of the non-indigenous population (excluding infections amongst people from high HIV prevalence countries). However, a significant proportion of HIV diagnoses among Aboriginal and Torres Strait Islander peoples are made up of IDUs (16 percent). Male to male contact accounts for 59 percent and heterosexual contact 17 percent. There is also a particularly high rate of HIV infection amongst females, with the Kirby Institute placing the figure at 21 percent (The Kirby Institute, 2012, p.19). Aboriginal Australians account for 2.3 percent of the total population. However, they make up 7 – 19 percent of samples captured by surveys of people who inject drugs (Paquette et al., 2012, p.1). They are also over represented in custodial settings where incidences of HIV can be higher as a result of un-sterile drug injecting and tattooing. A 2012 study found that Aboriginal people were less likely to know about blood- borne viruses, like HIV. However, it

137

also reported that Aboriginal people were no less likely than non-Aboriginal Australians to access services such as testing and drug treatment (Paquette et al., 2012, p.5).

## ART

The majority of people infected with HIV in Australia are receiving ART. The Australian HIV Observational Database reported that in 2011, 84.5 percent of the 2,032 people under follow-up were receiving triple combination antiretroviral treatment. (The Kirby Institute, 2012, p.31). The use of ART by men who have sex with men that participated in the Gay Community Periodic Surveys in 2011 has increased significantly. In 2007, 51.5 percent and 53.2 percent of gay men were using ART in Melbourne and Sydney respectively. In 2011, this had increased to 72.6 percent and 70.6 percent respectively (The Kirby Institute, 2012, p.31). Research shows that successful viral suppression on ART can reduce the risk of onward transmission of HIV to sex partners by up to 96 percent by decreasing the viral load (Down et al., 2012, p.8).

## The Official Response

The official response to HIV/AIDS can be seen as having been very successful with schemes introduced at both state and federal levels to assist in minimising the spread of the disease. During the 1980s, millions was spent on national education campaigns (Plate 6.1). Condom use was widely promoted on television during prime time viewing hours, sex and HIV/AIDS education courses were introduced in almost all secondary schools, and needle exchange programs were established across the country. Collectives of sex workers and IDUs also received funding to provide education and outreach support. Governments also took a pragmatic approach to HIV/AIDS prevention. This was perhaps best seen in the infamous *"Grim Reaper"* television commercial, where AIDS was portrayed as the *grim reaper* in an indoor bowling alley bowling down people who were arrayed as bowling pins. This highly striking shock-horror commercial strategy undoubtedly captured public attention and was part of a broader campaign coordinated by the National Advisory Committee on AIDS (NACAIDS) costing over $3.6 million, aimed at showing that HIV/AIDS did not discriminate between age, sex, or gender, and that prevention was the only means of combating the infection. Overall the campaign attracted some criticisms for seemingly exaggerating the risk of HIV/AIDS to ordinary Australians and for frightening children.

## Needle and Syringe Exchange

Needle and syringe exchange programs have become relatively widespread in Australia since 1986, when the first outlet opened in Darlinghurst Sydney, and are now considered to be among the most comprehensive in the world. Today, there are more than 3,000 such outlets across Australia, providing sterile injecting equipment, puncture-proof disposable containers, condoms, and information about safe sex. Over $130 million was invested in needle and syringe programs by Australian governments between 1991 and 2000 and such a program resulted in the prevention of an estimated 25,000 cases of HIV infection, saving the Australian health system between $2.2 and $7.7 billion (Doulan et al., 2005, p.4). Australia has managed to avoid the "second wave" of HIV infection amongst IDUs. Between 1999 and 2003, HIV prevalence among people attending needle and syringe programs remained around one percent, and less than 0.5 percent among men and women presenting at metropolitan sexual health clinics who identified themselves as IDUs (Doulan et al., 2005, p.5). This is a remarkably low figure when compared to other parts of the world, particularly Eastern Europe, where IDUs account for at least half of all infections (Sendziuk, 2002). The success of needle and syringe exchange programs in keeping down rates of HIV infection also had a flow-on effect of reducing cases where infection was transferred from mother to child. *The Sydney Morning Herald* reported in 1997 that whereas 17,000 paediatric cases had been observed in New York that year. New South Wales with a similar sized population had only 42 (Doulan et al., 2005, p.5).

The significant emphasis placed by Australian governments on risk reduction strategies, such as needle and syringe exchange programs, stemmed from the growing realisation that education campaigns alone were not enough to change the behaviour of people at risk from HIV/AIDS. A wide range of economic, legal and psychological factors made it difficult for those at risk of infection to make the behavioural choices that might keep them safe. Addicted IDUs would continue to share injecting equipment without the means to access or purchase sterile equipment, regardless of their understanding of the risks involved. Sex workers, despite their level of knowledge surrounding unsafe sexual practices, would find it difficult to insist on their clients wearing condoms. Also, gay men were unlikely to care for their health when they were often rejected and undervalued by the community at large. In order to achieve the necessary behavioural changes among risk groups, a number of initiatives were introduced along with needle and syringe exchange programs. Prostitution became legalised and/or liberalised to varying degrees across the country to ensure a safe working environment for sex workers, where condom use could be enforced and education on safe sex provided. Government funded workshops were run to nurture self-esteem within the gay community and empower those at risk. These initiatives were unique in so far as they moved the fight against HIV/AIDS from the traditional realm of doctors and medical researchers, and placed it directly in the hands of those at most at risk via the medium of peer education and community-based programs. Some States lingered behind in the adoption of such measures. For example, Queensland did not establish a needle and syringe program until 1990, and Tasmania not until three years later. Homosexuality only became legal across the entire country in 1997, when Tasmania finally changed its laws.

Both the state and federal government campaigns encountered criticism, including that the campaigns were not well targeted and did not provide information to particular groups, including non-English speaking people and homeless people. Also, right wing groups argued that education campaigns with an emphasis on condom use and needle exchange in fact supported the very practices that led to the spread of HIV/AIDS. In August 1985, former National Party leader Ian Sinclair, referring to the deaths of three babies in Queensland who had received transfusions of infected blood, was quoted in the *Sydney Morning Herald* as saying: "If it wasn't for the promotion of homosexuality as a norm by Labor, I am quite certain that the deaths of those poor babies would not have occurred" (Whitton, 1985, p.1). This gave rise to the tag line "LAIDS", or Labor-Acquired Immune Deficiency Syndrome. Overall, however, the official response can be regarded a success, with substantial increases in the rate of condom use and safe sex up amongst homosexual men by the end of the 1980s, with levels of infection falling dramatically during the 1990s.

## National Strategy Today

Australian governments have continued to place HIV/AIDS on the frontline of policy since 1989, when the first national strategy was released. The current national strategy, the Sixth National HIV Strategy to be released, which covered the years 2010 – 2013, builds on the previous five strategies with the overall goal to "reduce the transmission of and morbidity and mortality caused by HIV and to minimise the personal and social impact of HIV" (Australian Government Department of Health and Ageing, 2005, p.7). The particular approach adopted placed emphasis on the importance of establishing a productive partnership between people living with HIV, affected communities, the healthcare sector, researchers, and government. The involvement of people living with HIV was recognised as being particularly critical to developing a national strategy, as it ensured that policies and programs are effective and informed by those affected by HIV, meaning they are significantly more responsive to their exact needs. Such a strategy recognises that Australia has

140

reached a challenging period in its response to HIV/AIDS, with increasing rates of infection observed in a number of risk groups. This includes homosexual men and men who have sex with men, Australians travelling and working in high prevalence countries, some culturally and linguistically diverse (CALD) communities within Australia, and amongst IDUs in some Aboriginal and Torres Strait Islander communities.

A number of priority action areas were identified, each requiring a targeted approach. These include gay men and men who have sex with men, which requires the continued promotion of risk reduction and safe behaviour (Australian Government Department of Health and Ageing, 2010, p.21), and sex workers, where it is crucial to maintain low rates of infection (Australian Government Department of Health and Ageing, 2010, p.26). Attention is also directed towards people already living with HIV in order to prevent transmission, and to ensure that HIV-positive people are supported and included as partners in HIV health promotion, as well as Aboriginal and Torres Strait Islanders, who require their own specific approach that takes account of their unique epidemiology, natural history, and public health imperatives (Australian Government Department of Health and Ageing, 2010, p.5). Maintaining and expanding access for IDUs as well as other services and programs to help prevent further infections remains crucial (Australian Government Department of Health and Ageing, 2010, p.24). A particular focus is also placed on people in custodial settings, including jails and juvenile detention centres. HIV rates remain relatively low in such settings in Australia, however, the high turnover of inmates coupled with the frequency of risky practices, including injecting drugs, unsafe tattooing, unprotected sex, including sexual assault, and an overrepresentation of priority populations, namely Aboriginals and Torres Strait Islanders, remains a pressing issue (Australian Government Department of Health and Ageing, 2010, p.25). The strategy also commits attention to the professional development of HIV prevention and health promotion workers (Australian Government Department of Health and Ageing, 2010, p.28), continued monitoring of research developments (Australian Government Department of Health and Ageing, 2010, p.27), and an increasingly coordinated, accessible and affordable HIV diagnosis and testing system (Australian Government Department of Health and Ageing, 2010, p.28).

Targeted prevention measures are identified as being crucial to a successful national HIV strategy. When compared with other major health promotion programs, including tobacco control and heart disease prevention, investment in HIV prevention shows higher returns. A study measuring the impact of investment in HIV prevention in New South Wales projected that at least

44,500 infections had been avoided due to HIV prevention programs, and that for every dollar spent, $13 was saved (Australian Government Department of Health and Ageing, 2010, p.19). The strategy also outlines a number of new and emerging challenges facing policy makers, health professionals and individuals living with HIV. These include changing community perceptions about HIV, the impact of new therapies, increasingly diverse and diffuse gay communities, and challenges in reaching particular populations where emerging or re-emerging epidemics may be a problem (Australian Government Department of Health and Ageing, 2010, p.20). As well, the ageing of the overall population living with HIV raises a host of issues, as HIV can accelerate and compound the effects of ageing. In addition, elderly people with HIV often struggle to meet their healthcare costs while living on a pension or fixed retirement income (Australian Government Department of Health and Ageing, 2010, p.31).

## Plague Mentality and the Fear of Infection –The Human Reaction

What makes HIV/AIDS so distinctive is that unlike the other epidemic encounters described in this book, HIV/AIDS is a slow viral disease, extending over decades in a slow and insidious fashion targeting mainly young adults, particularly young males. It is also marked by its lethalness and the fact that it involves elements of human sex, blood and for some people, deviancy. Like all the other epidemics examined, HIV/AIDS is in effect two inter-twined epidemics – a demographic/epidemiological one producing cases and deaths, and a psycho-social component involving human reaction, hysteria and panic. For some time it appeared that the outpouring of human reaction, termed *AFRAIDS* (acute fear regarding AIDS) by *The New Republic* journal, would simply overwhelm the number of cases and deaths. The symptoms of *AFRAIDS* included avoidance, ostracism, discrimination, scapegoating and violence (*The New Republic*, 1985, p.7). In the case of HIV/AIDS, Australia had not experienced such a public display of human fear and emotion since the plague, influenza and polio epidemics of the early 20th century. 'Plague fear' as this book has been at pains to point out, is one of societies most basic fears, ingrained in our very psyche and HIV/AIDS tapped into this underlying fear and as Altman remarked, AIDS brought forth a mixture of rational fears regarding contagion and disease as well as irrational fears concerning sexuality and 'otherness' (Altman, 1986, p.59). Our human reaction to HIV/AIDS was largely governed by five major issues.

1. Generally held anxieties about contagion and disease and the difficulty of evaluating personal risk, exposure and vulnerability, and in particular the difficulty in comprehending

'official' statements re risk and exposure.

2.  Anxieties people have about 'otherness' and in particular people who pursue distinctively different life styles and personal behaviour particularly with respect to partners and sex.

3.  The media's presentation of HIV/AIDS and in particular the use of sensational language, imagery and placement.

4.  The fact that HIV/AIDS was presented as a 'new' hitherto unknown disease, of unknown origins, and for which no cure or specific treatment existed.

5.  The 'Armageddon' factor whereby HIV/AIDS was presented as the 'wrath of god' and the 'plague to end all plagues.'

What is disturbing about fear is that it rarely comes undiluted but is invariably manipulated and exploited. As a consequence, its objects become displaced and its functions perverted. During the 1980s the Australian newspapers regularly ran stories about the *gay plague,* when for some the real message was *the plague of gays.* Discussion about HIV/AIDS was invested with moral judgements and AIDS became a metaphor for something much more sinister – a form of double jeopardy where first you suffer the effects of the disease and then you suffer the stigma which follows. When HIV/AIDS first emerged in Australia in the early 1980s, there was a significant lack of public knowledge and understanding of HIV, its origins and how it was transmitted. This led to widespread misguided public opinion and instilled an irrational fear of HIV/AIDS amongst some members of the Australian public. Public ignorance of HIV/AIDS led in some instances to discrimination towards people living with HIV, or presumed to have HIV. A wave of fear and paranoia swept through cities like Sydney.

There were many reported instances during the mid-1980s of people being denied the right to remain in lawful employment, banned from attending schools, or refused housing, insurance and dental services as well as being refused entry to bars and discos. Discrimination was also seen in some hospitals responsible for treating HIV/AIDS patients where in some cases, patients' meals were simply left outside the door to their room, they were given disposable crockery and cutlery, and had their sheets double bagged and washed in a separate washing machine. Postal workers expressed concern about having to handle letters where the seal and stamps might have been licked by an AIDS sufferer. Sydney plumbers also refused to service and repair public toilets and all Qantas staff on board flights refused to distribute and handle hot towels. Rubbish collectors reportedly feared infection from needles and syringes being disposed of in the garbage. However, in reality, the virus would be long dead by the time the rubbish collectors came into contact with it.

Sport too was not excluded from the public paranoia. In Queensland cricket umpires were exempted from holding players' boxes (groin protectors) during cricket matches for fear of AIDS contamination. A survey carried out in 1987 revealed the extent of public misunderstanding and ignorance about HIV/AIDS. Of the 178 respondents surveyed, 20 percent were certain that one could catch AIDS by living with an infected person and a significant proportion of respondents were unsure about how HIV/AIDS was actually contracted, and pointed their finger at everyday things like sharing linen, sneezing, and sharing a toilet seat. The survey also revealed the attitudes people felt towards the homosexual community, many regarding casual sex among homosexuals more risky than casual heterosexual intercourse (Heaven 1987, p. 273).

Perhaps the most well known story of HIV/AIDS-related discrimination in Australia was that of Eve Van Grafhorst, a young girl who became HIV positive following a blood transfusion as a baby. In 1985 she became embroiled in a storm of controversy when she was banned from attending her local kindergarten in Kincumber, New South Wales, amid fears that she might infect other children. After numerous threats from other parents that they would withdraw their children from the kindergarten, Eve was forced to wear a plastic facemask. In the end she was expelled from the kindergarten for playfully biting a friend. The Van Grafhorst family also faced considerable discrimination from their neighbours, and in 1986 made a decision to relocate to Hawkes Bay, New Zealand, where they lived in a supporting environment until Eve died of AIDS aged 11 in 1993.

The human reaction to HIV/AIDS in Australia in the 1980s largely followed a similar path to traditional human reactions to epidemics of infectious diseases. An initial phase of denial was followed by a period of fear and hysteria, and the search for scapegoats. In the case of HIV, the homosexual community became the scapegoat and because homosexuals were the group at most risk from HIV, it was transformed into a gay issue and referred to in some circles as the "*gay plague*". Among sectors of the Australian population homosexuality was seen to be synonymous with evil, sickness and sin, and many felt that all homosexuals should be strictly avoided (Kayal, 1985, p.219). A father whose child died of AIDS following a blood transfusion in 1984 was quoted in a Sydney newspaper, saying "As far as I am concerned the homosexuals are sick people and should be treated like lepers. They should be left on an island to die" (*The Sydney Morning Herald*, 1984, p.4). A leading Sydney clergyman labelled AIDS as the 'wrath of God disease', stating that "homosexual men by their sexual behaviour have rebelled against God's creative plan and by their actions shaken their fist in the face of God" (*Sydney Morning Herald*, 24 February 1987, p.1). However, this negative attitude towards homosexuals by some members of the Australian public had a positive impact on the gay community which utilised this stigma to generate solidarity and support for each other amongst their community.

The stigma faced by people infected with HIV, or belonging to a group at risk of contracting the disease, served as a major obstacle to combating HIV/ AIDS. People went out of their way to avoid being tested for HIV and, if they did test positive, they often went to great lengths to avoid disclosing such information. Stigma and discrimination also often forced those at the highest risk of contracting HIV, including sex workers, injecting drug users, and homosexual men, to conceal their lifestyles. This made it exceedingly difficult to reach them through HIV/AIDS education and prevention programs (Lamptey et al., 2002, p. 9). The stigma felt by people who had been diagnosed with HIV could have tragic consequences, such as the four cases of post-HIV diagnosis suicides reported in South Australia in 1986 (Hailstone, 1986, p. 1).

People living with HIV/AIDS still experience stigma today. In September 2012, the National Association of People Living with AIDS (NAPWA) released The HIV Stigma Audit. It revealed that HIV sufferers, and those belonging to groups that are at high risk of being infected with HIV, still report feelings of being ashamed, blamed, avoided, rejected, and excluded in society. Some also still observe negative experiences resulting from the lingering "media memory" (Slavin et al., 2012, p.20).

## The Legal System

A number of potential legal issues associated with HIV/AIDS were recognised in the early 1980s when the epidemic first appeared in Australia. All Australians are responsible for preventing HIV transmission under the law, and over the past two decades there have been approximately 30 criminal cases involving HIV. These cases have not involved charges that specifically mention HIV, but instead have been usually classified under other categories such as, causing grievous bodily harm, causing serious harm or injury, and endangerment. A number of concerns have been raised relating to the criminalisation of HIV. In a report for the Australian Federation of AIDS Organisations, Sally Cameron raised a concern that the fear of potential prosecution would reduce the willingness of an individual to disclose their HIV status, which has the potential to increase the rates of HIV transmission (Cameron, 2011, p.11). A NAPWA report also raised a number of issues, including the highly discriminatory nature of criminal cases relating to HIV transmission. Blame and persecution is directed solely toward the HIV positive person, which NAPWA deems unacceptable as it goes against 20 years of working for and developing a public health approach towards HIV/AIDS that focuses on shared responsibility and safe, consensual sex.

The media coverage of criminal cases involving HIV often created further issues as it tended to reinforce the belief that the responsibility for preventing HIV transmission lies solely with HIV positive people. This shifted the focus away from a cooperative public health approach, and provides misinformation, only adding a further burden to those already living with and having to cope with a stigmatised disease (Cameron and Rule, 2009, p. 24). The NAPWA report suggests that HIV should be kept away from the realm of the courts, except for cases of wilful transmission (Cameron and Rule, 2009, p.25).

## Making a Profit during Times of Crisis

In times of epidemic crisis the manufacturers and purveyors of products and services are quick to take advantage of the opportunity for financial profit. Such was the case with HIV/AIDS. Following global increases in condom sales, the president of condom manufacturer Ansell America, John Silverman, stated that "AIDS is a condom marketer's dream" (*The Sydney Morning Herald*, 1987, p.14). In 1985, Australians purchased 17 million condoms, 15 percent more than the previous year, and an investment of $7 million (O'Neill, 1986, p.13). In November 1985 Lifestyles Condoms ran a full page advertisement in the *Sydney Morning Herald* extolling the virtues of condom use headed "*A.I.D.S. and Condoms*". Two months after its listing on the stock market, the Private Blood Bank's shares skyrocketed an incredible 3,040 percent as the spread and fear of AIDS infection via blood transfusion gripped Australia in 1987 (Hely 1987, p. 41). The federal government's AIDS Coordinating Unit approved the tenders of nine companies to produce HIV testing kits and 1,500,000 kits were sold in 1985, retailing for between $1.40 and $2.60 (O'Neill 1986, p.13).

Other commercial exploits took full advantage of the fear and hysteria surrounding AIDS. Overseas, a Los Angeles based firm sold identification cards guaranteeing the bearer was HIV-free. These cards had to be renewed every three months at a cost of $45 (*United Press* 1986, p. 3). Bogus diet plans claiming to 'cure' AIDS, false charities, and useless home testing kits were also distributed in North America (Mullens, 1985, p.10). HIV/AIDS also meant big business for drug companies despite the fact that over the last decade prices have fallen significantly as a result of the production of generic or cheap copies of anti-retroviral drugs, and favourable pricing policies by

146

pharmaceutical companies. This has meant ART has, to some extent, become more accessible and affordable to people in developing countries. But multinational drug companies continue to rake in large profits, with ART sales across the seven major markets of the United States, Japan, France, Germany, Spain, Italy, and the UK totalling US$11.8 billion in 2009 (Kumar 2010).

## The Media and the Cult of Disease

The media has always played a significant role in raising public awareness and shaping peoples' perceptions of infectious disease in Australia and HIV/ AIDS was no exception. As Altman and Humphrey remarked, "AIDS was socially constructed in Australia as essentially a "gay disease", a construction of which, as elsewhere, the Murdoch press played a considerable role" (Altman and Humphrey, 1989, p.159). During the early 1980s, sensationalist and alarmist media headlines helped nurture in the Australian public a sense of apprehension and fear. On August 1st 1985, for example, the front page of *The Australian* carried the banner headline *"AIDS epidemic could rival the Black Death"* (*The Australian*, 1985, p.1). Two days later the same newspaper ran the headline *"Plague of the millennium: AIDS is with us forever"* (*The Australian*, 3 August, 1985, p.4). Other media reports that contributed to the public perception of HIV/AIDS include *The Daily Mirror's* story from July 1985, titled *"AIDS FEAR HITS RBT PATROLS"*, reporting on the decline in random breath testing by police, and the introduction of gloves and the use of disinfection during patrols that were conducted (Kerr, 1985, p.1). The story *"Lifeguards gear against AIDS"* was reported on the front page of *The Manly Daily* in August 1985 (Ryan and Cox 1985, p.1) and in October the *Daily Telegraph* followed with *"Cricket hits out at AIDS"*, which covered the move by Queensland umpires to stop holding players' groin protectors to prevent contamination (Jones 1985, p.3). In December 1985 *The Sun* Newspaper ran the banner headline *"AIDS TESTS FOR ALL'* in response to a comment from the New South Wales Premier Neville Wran calling for all Australians to be tested for AIDS (*THE SUN*, 13 December 1985, p.1). Sensationalist media reports such as these exacerbated the negative perception of HIV/AIDS held by the Australian public. In 1995, the Australian Federation of AIDS Organisations published the first edition of a set of guidelines for journalists on reporting on HIV/AIDS in Australia. Revised in 2000, 2009 and 2011, the purpose of these guidelines was to ensure that journalists would provide full, accurate, and intelligent coverage of HIV, and challenge common myths and misinformation. A number of "do's and don'ts" for reporting on HIV/AIDS were emphasised, including not to confuse HIV and AIDS, avoid stereotyping, to take care with language and data, and to respect confidentiality (Forbes, 2011,p. 2). Today, HIV/AIDS does not appear in the Australian media in the same sensationalist manner that characterised the 1980s.

## Conclusion

HIV/AIDS is without any doubt a devastating human tragedy throughout the world and despite medical advances in treatment as well as official campaigns to raise public awareness, the disease continues to spread. It is also the first time Australian society has been confronted by an epidemic of a slow viral disease extending over decades. In many ways AIDS is also a significant signpost of the difficulty that many societies such as Australia encounter when confronted by deeply entrenched public attitudes about personal behaviour, risk and anxiety about infectious disease. It also raises the important question as to how society can strive to maintain some sort of equilibrium between individual rights and liberties and the overall health and wellbeing of all the population.

CHAPTER 7

# Nature Bites Back:
# From SARS to Swine Flu

In 1967 the US Surgeon-General proudly announced to an American nation that the time had come to close the book on infectious diseases, that infectious diseases had been virtually wiped out in the USA, and that it was time to move on and address a range of important chronic diseases like cancer and heart disease that were confronting society. In fact as many of us in the developed world indulged visions of a new infection-free age, new infections were already appearing. At first they appeared in Africa and Asia, but with our Western ethnocentric vision we could conveniently ignore them. But then in the 1970s everything changed and a wide range of "new" infections burst forth and our complacency was dashed forever.

Looking back on the early 1950s there were plenty of signposts of emerging infections which we tended to overlook or totally ignore. West Nile virus, for example, burst forth in a series of major epidemics in Israel between 1950 and 1954 (see Cameron, 2001, pp.1289-1290). Korean hemorrhagic fever appeared in 1951 in a classical example of how war and related population movements could totally disrupt a natural disease environment and release a "new" infection (see Traub and Wisseman, 1978, pp.267-272). Dengue hemorrhagic fever appeared two years later as did Junin virus in Argentina in 1953 where it killed up to 20 percent of all its victims (see Romanowski, 1993, pp. 51-52). In addition, a number of exotic infections appeared in

India, Uganda and Brazil. It was not until 1967, however, when a "new" and particularly virulent hemorrhagic fever appeared in Zaire and the Sudan only to make world headlines when it affected 31 workers in a research laboratory in Marburg, Germany, that our attention was finally captured (see WHO, Marburg Hemorrhagic Fever).

The next three decades would witness a seemingly unending parade of "new" infections such as La Cross Encephalitis, Australian Murray Valley encephalitis, Lassa Fever, Lyme Disease, Ebola, Legionnaires Disease, Toxic Shock Syndrome, and HIV/AIDS. By the beginning of the 21st century it was fast becoming clear that the promise of an infection-free age had proved illusionary and within a few years the world would be faced with epidemics of SARS, Avian Flu and Swine Flu.

In mid 2001, two years before SARS emerged on an unsuspecting world, Thomas Eisner and Paul Ehrlich published a short satirical editorial in the journal *Science* on the resurgence of infectious disease. Their comment claimed to be based on a recently received document from the World Convention of the Pathogen Association entitled *"Our Infective Future: The New Agenda"*. At the Convention, the president of the Pathogen Association (suitably named President Prion) in an opening address to the delegates, stated:-

"I must inform the infective community… that most of our natural hosts are disappearing. Never has our future been bleaker, threatened as it is by a reality that was unthinkable 5,000 years ago. Our food supplies are being displaced by a single species, Homo Sapiens … Action is called for. Indeed in this disaster there is the germ of an opportunity and an opportunity for germs. In our evolutionary tradition, we must prepare ourselves to change our tastes, shift hosts, and take advantage of the single most appealing and available addition to our menu. Homophagia is the way of the future… some congratulations are in order … To HIV for killing slowly enough to share the host with many of the rest of us. To the Tuberculosis bacillus for its unexpected renewed success. To the viruses – Ebola, Hanta, Lassa and Marburg – for their gallant efforts. To Legionella for … its stealth [and had he been speaking today he might well have added – SARS, Avian and Swine Flu as well]… And to those already at the trough – the great pioneers such as Plasmodium, the dengue virus, and Treponema, and especially that great debilitator, the common cold virus – for setting splendid examples to ensure that success is within the grasp of us all. There are many factors that give us hope. Homo is remarkably hospitable to us. In extraordinary numbers they are now undernourished and immunodeficient, and they have a penchant for keeping on the move providing many new opportunities for the novices among us to join the feast ... They misuse antibiotics, among their very best weapons against us, blind to our evolutionary capacity to develop resistance. They pay little attention to our important ability to evolve new levels of virulence. And they are recklessly changing the climate, releasing many of us from our historical geographical constraints ..." (Eisner and Erhlich, 2001, p.2397).

How true and how relevant such a comment sounds today, when barely a month passes by without the emergence of some "new" microbiological threat to human health and wellbeing, or when we experience the resurgence of some long-established infections thought to have long disappeared or to be under our control. But few people in 2001 could have foreseen that the world would struggle with three major epidemic/pandemic threats during the first decade of the new century and that our confidence would be stretched to near breaking point. HIV/AIDS set the scene in the early 1980s through to today and it was the first time that the world had been confronted by a slow viral pandemic. Among other things it revealed just how fragile was our understanding of viral infections and how poorly organised our response mechanisms were. It also brought home to us how the media could play a decisive role in influencing human behaviour and reaction.

## SARS

For a number of months in the first half of 2003, SARS, a 'new' viral respiratory infection of humans caused by a coronavirus, dominated the world's headlines with reports of a growing epidemic largely concentrated in China, Hong Kong, Taiwan and parts of East Asia. The disease was first recognised in Fushan city in Guangdong Province in China in November 2002 and after spreading to Hong Kong in mid February 2003 the virus spread to more than 30 countries (See Shannon and Willoughby, 2005, pp. 364-375). In total, SARS produced more than 8,400 cases and caused at least 916 deaths in a little over five months (Figure 7.1), (WHO: Summary SARS cases, 2004). Overall, 95 percent of all SARS cases and 94 percent of all deaths occurred in China, Hong Kong, Taiwan and Singapore, with China/Hong Kong alone contributing 84 percent. As in the case of traditional influenza, it was the elderly who were most at risk with the death rate approaching 44 percent for those aged over 60 years

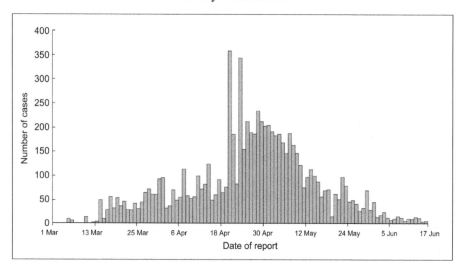

**Figure 7.1** Number of Probable SARS Cases in the World, 2003.

Notably fewer than four percent of cases and deaths occurred outside China/ East Asia and Canada. Health care workers were particularly at risk. In Taiwan, for example, 90 percent of cases occurred in hospitals and at one point 20 percent of those infected in Hong Kong were nurses (Shannon and Willoughby, 2005, pp. 367-368 and 372-374). Generally SARS spread from an epicentre in South China via hospital-based infections, in a contagious-cascading fashion, spreading outwards from index cases, following well-defined routes reflecting the geographic mobility of infected individuals and their interaction with family members, business contacts and hospital staff. Like most respiratory infections SARS spread via droplet secretions, face to face contact and contaminated surfaces.

It seems likely that SARS emerged in the live animal markets in Guangdong province in China. In such markets, cages of bats, civets, racoons, badgers and other animals were usually stacked on top of each other in close proximity to chickens and other birds. The opportunity for the viral transfer between different species in such a context must have been considerable. In late January a 44 year-old seafood seller, who had been hospitalised with what turned out to be SARS, passed the virus on to 19 relatives and 50 or more hospital workers (Zhao et.al, 2003, p.716). Three weeks later one of the doctors who treated him in hospital travelled to Hong Kong. During a one night stay on the 9th floor of the Metropole Hotel he infected 17 people and with a few weeks the virus had spread beyond Hong Kong to Singapore, Vietnam, the Philippines and Canada (Mackenzie, et.al, 2004, p.43). In Canada an elderly woman who had had the misfortune to be a guest at the Metropole Hotel in Hong Kong at the same time as the Chinese doctor, died on February 21$^{st}$. Officially her cause of death was recorded as a heart attack, but before she died she had passed the infection on to four members of her family. Two days later her son went to the Emergency Room of a local hospital and by the time he was seen by medical staff he had already passed the virus to three other people in the room. Believed to be only suffering from TB or a respiratory infection he was transferred to another hospital where he infected more than 50 people (Shaw, 2007, p.51).

Within a few weeks more than 251 Canadians would catch SARS and 41 would die from the disease. Significantly, nearly 100 hospital workers in three Toronto hospitals became ill with SARS largely through contact with infected patients or family members. Unlike China, Canada did not delineate specific hospitals as SARS Hospitals during the outbreak but instead simply designated specific wards for SARS cases. By contrast, in Australia only six cases of SARS were recorded with no deaths. SARS affected people in a variety of ways. All patients presented with extremely high temperatures and many suffered fever, chills, malaise, shortness of breath and in some cases anorexia, vomiting and diarrhoea.

What was unique about SARS was the epidemic of fear and hysteria it produced. In part this was engendered by the "shock of the new", and in part by long-standing fears about "plague", infection and contagion. But coming when it did, the human reaction to SARS was undoubtedly influenced by the global 'climate of fear' that had emerged in the world following the events of September 11$^{th}$, the so-called 'war on terror', the Bali Bombing and the widespread publicity given to the possible release of a bioterrorist agent following the anthrax scare in the USA. There is little doubt that fear also fed the various efforts of national governments to control and contain the epidemic. Ironically, governments made recourse to traditional public health measures typically associated with epidemics prior to the 1950s, such as isolation and quarantine of affected patients and their contacts, scavenging, disinfecting and cleansing of suspected infected areas and public places, recommendations regarding personal hygiene and the wearing of masks and increased public surveillance. Such measures had a high public profile and undoubtedly played a part in influencing peoples' perception of risk and fear of infection. In Canada more than 15,000 people were formally instructed to remain in voluntary quarantine in their homes for up to four weeks. They were told not to leave their homes, to wash their hands frequently, to wear masks when mixing with other family members, not to share eating utensils and towels and to sleep in separate rooms. Such restrictions undoubtedly took a considerable toll on the wellbeing of those quarantined. Being physically cut off from relatives, friends and work colleagues produced considerable depression and psychological distress (see, for example, Hawryluck et.al, 2004, pp.1206-1212).

Fear operated at a variety of levels. At the economic level, SARS had a major impact on business throughout the ASEAN area and beyond, causing substantial damage to airlines, tourism, and the hotel and entertainment industries. ASEAN countries lost between $US20 and $30 Billion while Hong Kong's growth rate fell from three percent to 1.5 percent. A wide variety of businesses that either used Asia as their centre of production, or who marketed their products in the region were particularly affected. It was the first time that business realised that they would have to build into their activities a new layer of risk management concerned with infectious disease. But it was at the personal level that SARS had its greatest impact. Fear of contracting SARS influenced peoples' behaviour making them avoid public places, as well as travel and face to face contact. In Hong Kong, Singapore and parts of China schools closed, public meetings were abandoned or postponed, while restaurants and shopping areas suffered heavily from a fall in patronage. Tourism, air transport and retailing were the hardest hit sectors as consumers shunned shopping, restaurants, entertainment venues and travellers cancelled trips (See Figure 7.2). Cathay Pacific suspended 45 percent of its flights and in May, Singapore Airlines cut capacity by 71 percent and placed more than 6,000 flight staff on unpaid leave. Qantas was recorded as losing about $A1 million a week in lost fares, while Air New Zealand saw its profits slashed by 13 percent (*The Australian*, 16 May, 2005, p.27). The World Bank estimated China's SARS-related losses at $US14 Billion (See Fan, 2003, pp.1-10). SARS brought back all the classical human reactions to epidemics – fear, panic, flight, isolation, avoidance, rumour-mongering and scapegoating, as well as a wide variety of personal adjustment strategies. People were reported trying to flee from Hong Kong, while international companies withdrew many of their staff. Other companies such as Wal-Mart formally banned any of its staff from visiting China, Hong Kong, Singapore, Vietnam, and even Canada.

Violent confrontations and looting were reported in parts of China. In scenes reminiscent of earlier plague epidemics, teams of robed and masked scavengers and cleansers descended on quarantined buildings and adjacent public areas. Elsewhere people resorted to masks, gloves and excessive hand washing and social distancing became the order of the day as people avoided crowds and public places. In Hong Kong SARS produced an obsession with hygiene and cleanliness which saw anti-microbial soap dispensers installed in public places, disinfected floor mats placed outside public buildings and plastic sheeting placed over lift buttons. A number of countries such as Kazakhstan and Kyrgyzstan formally closed their borders with China. Singapore Airlines took to issuing "health kits" to passengers on flights to and from cities affected by SARS. All around the world Governments issued travel advisories to avoid certain places while people stocked up with disinfectants, bleach and patent medicines.

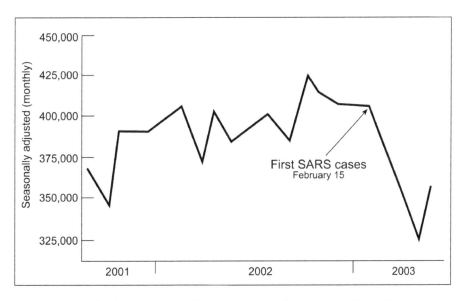

**Figure 7.2** Decline in Short-Term Visitors to Australia Because of SARS, 2001-2003.

Faced with the inability of health authorities to provide a cure or a satisfactory explanation of the disease, people turned to traditional medicines and popular cures. In China droves of people turned to herbal tonics as well as employing sorcerers and firecrackers to drive away malign spirits. Many companies were quick to realise the commercial possibilities of the epidemic and marketed a wide range of SARS preventatives and treatments including air purifiers, herbal remedies and dietary supplements. At one stage there were also 48 internet sites in Canada offering everything from air purifiers to dietary supplements as SARS "cures". Anxiety and fear also brought to the surface old tensions and antagonisms. The search for scapegoats or someone to blame took on a life of its own and people began to blame the Chinese and avoid Chinatowns. During the height of the Canadian outbreak the Canadian media began to refer to *"The Yellow Peril"* and there were reports of the Chinese being verbally abused on Toronto streets. In the USA people began to boycott Chinese restaurants. The desire to find someone to blame became all pervading. *"Super-Spreaders"* in particular were sought out and identified. In Singapore an individual was even officially named as being responsible for introducing SARS to the island state and subsequently assumed *"Typhoid Mary"* status.

Even cities such as Beijing, Hong Kong and Toronto took on the mantle of "pariah infected cities" and were scrupulously avoided. In New Zealand, backpackers from China were refused accommodation at a Hostel. In all of this the media played an important role. The desire to play on peoples' emotions proved irresistible. Every day during April we were confronted by newspaper headlines such as - *"Killer virus on the loose"*, *"Every breath you take"*, *"The China Syndrome"*, *"The cough heard around the world"*, *"the cold that kills"*, as well as being confronted by seemingly endless images of doctors in masks and goggles, of deserted shopping malls, quarantined buildings, and health teams monitoring airport arrivals. All this language and imagery presented daily preyed on the public imagination. SARS threw up a host of vivid and striking images from the past – quarantine, masks, scavenging and cleaning teams of workers, and restrictions on human movement. Although there is very little humour in epidemic outbreaks, SARS managed to throw up one or two classic moments such as the CBS News Report on May 9th that a shortage of masks in Southern China had caused factories to stop making female bras and switch to making masks. The report added that while waiting for the masks, some people were actually using the bras as face masks. Mandarin Films in Hong Kong planned to make a comedy-drama about SARS called *The City of SARS*, a love story where two people meet when they are forced into quarantine. At a WHO Virtual Press Briefing in Geneva on May 17th 2003, the WHO Co-ordinator of the WHO Global Alert and Response Program while discussing the possible transmission route of SARS stated that "… In certain circumstances, the aerosolization of faecal matter may have a role". To which a wit later added that it was just as well that SARS was prefixed by an "S". In the final analysis SARS was something of a minor epidemiological affair. It only affected about 8,000 people, mortality was low, and infectivity not very high, and those most at risk were older people suffering from impaired cardiovascular and respiratory systems. But the "shock of the new" and the human reaction that the disease engendered overwhelmed all other aspects of the outbreak.

The WHO declared SARS to have been eradicated in 2005. Whether the disease just disappeared from human sight and simply retreated back into its natural animal reservoir to perhaps reappear in future years is open to debate. Among other things, SARS provided us with a taste of what was to come and it taught us much about how ill-prepared we were to deal with a newly emerged infection that spread fairly quickly around the world. SARS also raised many questions about the links between animal and human health. It also told us much about how the media in a 24/7 world can transform a relatively minor health crisis into a major human pandemic of fear and hysteria.

## Avian Flu

Every year, normal seasonal flu usually burns its way through the Australian community in about 6-10 weeks during the winter months, affecting between 5 and 10 percent of the population largely as a mild and largely self-limiting infection. Occasionally, epidemics occur when the disease sweeps through the whole country. During pandemics, the disease infects a large percentage of the world's population. In Australia during past flu pandemics up to 35 percent of the population was affected. The world has experienced at least 10 major flu pandemics over the last 300 years. The last four, in 1889-91, 1918-19, 1957-58 and 1967-68, were all caused by the H1, H2 and H3 viruses (Figure 7.3). The pandemics that affected Australia in 1890-91 and 1919 were particularly severe. The 1890-91 pandemic was the first time Australia had experienced a country-wide pandemic and few families escaped its ravages. As Chapter 3 has demonstrated, the 1918-19 pandemic was a major demographic and social tragedy for the entire world, with perhaps as many as 80 million people dying from flu or complications, including more than 15,000 in Australia. At the height of the 1919 pandemic, between 30 and 35 percent of all people in Sydney and Melbourne were infected.

Avian flu, or bird flu as it became commonly known, is a contagious animal disease that infects birds and some mammals. The disease is a classic zoonosis which has probably been maintained in natural reservoirs in parts of Asia for centuries. Wild waterfowl such as ducks, geese, gulls and shorebirds are the normal host of influenza A viruses and it would appear that such viruses permanently circulate among such birds. Domestic poultry would seem to be particularly susceptible to the virus and in the case of ducks, remain asymptomatic. In its natural state, the virus circulates among its primary host – waterfowl, largely as a benign asymptomatic gastrointestinal infection. The virus is particularly well adapted to its host's life cycle and environment, rarely causing death, and existing continuously in a state of mutual adaptation and tolerance. Waterfowl would seem to transport the virus over great distances, excreting it in their droppings while remaining perfectly healthy (FAO, 2005, pp.1-7). The transmission chain among birds follows a faecal-oral route, often via the medium of virus-contaminated waterways or surface water.

Even when transmitted to local domestic poultry, the virus rarely produced more than a mild disease, with perhaps a slight decline in egg production.

157

From time to time, however, a more pathogenic strain of the virus emerged, probably as a result of a series of mutation events in its natural host or among infected poultry. In such circumstances, avian flu was transformed into an overwhelming systemic and frequently fatal disease. The highly pathogenic form of the disease was first documented in Italy in 1878 following a number of outbreaks in the Po Valley, and was referred to as 'fowl plague' or 'Lombardian disease' ( Perroncito, 1878, pp.87-126). It was not until the mid 1950s, however, that the causative agent was formally identified as Influenza A virus (Scaffer, 1955, pp.81-91). Since 1959 there have been at least 27 outbreaks of the highly pathogenic form of avian flu, the majority in Europe or America, but including four in Australia (Table 7.1). In 2014-15 the USA also suffered one of its worst outbreaks of avian flu with millions of domestic birds affected forcing the USA to cull millions of domestic poultry birds to stop the infection spreading. Some years later in 2021-23 avian flu again reared its head in the USA the infection spreading throughout the USA, the UK and EU causing at least 140 million bird deaths.

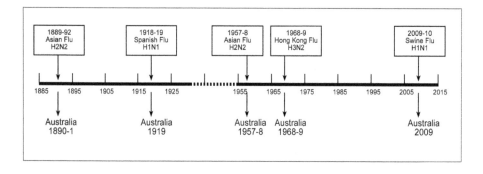

**Figure 7.3** Influenza Pandemics and Australia, 1889-2009

Most outbreaks were limited in geographical extent, and to date, all outbreaks of the highly pathogenic form of the virus have involved the H5 and H7 subtypes. In many cases these outbreaks involved substantial numbers of domestic poultry, such as in Holland in 2003 when more than 30 million birds were affected or in Pennsylvania in 1983-85 when more than 17 million birds were involved (see Harder and Werner, 2006). In the 2005 outbreak possibly hundreds of millions of wild and domestic birds became infected. The virus has also demonstrated considerable resilience and robustness in its ability to adapt to environmental change, in particular having the ability to survive temperature extremes, remaining latent in freezing conditions, only to reactivate when conditions improved.

| Year | Location | Viral Strain | No. of Birds Affected |
|------|----------|--------------|----------------------|
| 1959 | Scotland | H5N1 | Small number |
| 1963 | England | H7N3 | 29,000 turkeys |
| 1966 | Ontario | H5N9 | 8,000+ turkeys |
| 1976 | Australia (Victoria) | H7N7 | 40,000+ chickens/ducks |
| 1979 | Germany | H7N7 | 600,000+ chickens |
| 1979 | England | H7N7 | Not stated |
| 1983-85 | Pennsylvania | H5N2 | 17,000,000+ chickens/turkeys |
| 1983 | Ireland | H5N8 | 300,000+ chickens/ turkeys |
| 1985 | Australia (Victoria) | H7N7 | 200,000+ chickens |
| 1991 | England | H5N1 | 8,000 turkeys |
| 1992 | Australia (Victoria) | H7N3 | 20,000 chickens/ducks |
| 1994 | Australia (Queensland) | H7N3 | 22,000 chickens |
| 1994-95 | Mexico | H5N2 | Not stated |
| 1994 | Pakistan | H7N3 | 3,000,000+ chickens |
| 1997 | Hong Kong | H5N1 | 1,500,000+ chickens/birds |
| 1997 | Australia (NSW) | H7N4 | 60,000+ chickens/emus |
| 1997 | Italy | H5N2 | 6,000+ chickens |
| 1999-00 | Italy | H7N1 | 14,000,000 chickens |
| 2002 | Chile | H7N3 | Not stated |
| 2003 | Holland | H7N7 | 30,000,000+ chickens |
| 2004 | Canada | H7N3 | 17,000,000+ chickens |
| 2004 | USA | H5N2 | 6,000+ chickens |
| 2004 | South Africa | H5N2 | 29,000+ chickens/ostrich |
| 2002-07 | Asia, Africa, Europe | H5N1 | 250,000,000+ wild birds and domestic poultry. |
| 2014-15 | USA | H5N8 | More than 58,000.000 domestic bird deaths |
| 2021-23 | World | H5N1 | More than 140,000,000 bird deaths. |

**Table 7.1:** Outbreaks of Pathogenic Avian Influenza

Source: After Harder and Werner, 2006. CDC Avian Flu.

In April 2005 several thousand geese and other bird species at Lake Qinghai in North-Western China succumbed to avian flu. Over the next few months outbreaks were reported in geographically adjacent areas, and later in countries further afield. The diffusion mechanism of most of these outbreaks seemed to correlate closely with the normal migratory fly-paths of wild birds. Where domestic poultry became infected it usually occurred in close proximity to lakes and marshes inhabited or visited by, waterfowl. The actual role of the virus in populations of such birds, however, still remains poorly understood, and the role of migratory birds in spreading the virus over considerable geographical distances remains unresolved and so far no healthy migratory birds have tested positive for H5N1.

During 2005-06, a debate emerged about the role of traditional backyard or free-range poultry raising versus industrial poultry practices as an integral part of the engine driving the current wave of avian flu outbreaks. Generally it has been assumed that the chain of infection from wild birds to domestic poultry reflected inter-species encounters as such birds interacted freely, often sharing the same water source. Recently, some have argued that the confinement of poultry and other animals in huge factory farms throughout parts of Asia, and the recycling of poultry litter in animal feed, has encouraged virus mutation and exchange, accelerating the possibility of antibiotic resistant strains, and providing a fertile environment for the emergence of new infections (See GRAIN, 2006, pp.1-9). Since the early 1960s, the world poultry population has increased fourfold to roughly 18 Billion birds, and at the same time farming methods have changed, and the traditional relationship that domestic poultry once enjoyed with their local environment radically altered.

The globalisation of poultry production over the last few decades has been staggering. In Thailand, Vietnam and Indonesia, production increased from around 300,000 metric tonnes of chicken meat in 1971 to more than 2,400,000 metric tonnes in 2001, while China's chicken production tripled in the 1990s to more than 9 million metric tonnes a year (GRAIN, 2006, p.2). Most of this development has occurred on factory farms with upwards of 30,000 birds raised in battery conditions. Thailand and Brazil have seen the rapid industrialisation of their livestock industries in recent years. Poultry raising on intensive factory farms with units of 30-50,000 birds has become common. Thailand has also become a major exporter of chicken meat to Western Europe. In 2003, for example, Thailand exported 545,000 metric tonnes of poultry meat (see USDA, 2006). It would also seem likely that "wet" markets where live birds of different species are kept close to each other in crowded conditions, would act as a multiplier effect.

## A Human Pandemic in Waiting?

The widespread nature and virulence of avian flu in both wild and domestic birds, and the handful of human cases and deaths gave rise to concerns that we were approaching a situation where the virus might jump to affect human populations and initiate a human pandemic of influenza. The outbreak of avian flu came close to fulfilling three essential conditions for causing a human flu pandemic. Firstly, a new influenza subtype emerged to which humans had little or no immunity. Secondly, this new viral subtype developed the ability to replicate in humans and cause serious illness. Thirdly and most critically, to this point the virus has not developed the ability to be effectively transmitted from one human to another. There would seem to be two routes for avian flu to meet this third critical condition. One is that the virus encounters a human flu virus and re-assorts, perhaps by way of an intermediary species, such as pigs, into a new virulent human virus. Why this did not happen remains something of a mystery given that the pathogenic strain of the avian flu virus had ample time and opportunity for such an encounter. Secondly, the virus might be able to develop the ability to jump directly to human populations, in much the same way as seems to have happened in the 1918-19 Influenza pandemic.

The virus responsible for the 1918-19 human pandemic was an avian flu virus, and arguably it took the virus a number of years prior to 1918 to develop the capacity to directly infect humans. The chances of one of these things happening in future years would seem related to the amount of avian flu virus circulating in wild birds and domestic poultry and the continued exposure of human populations. In 2006 a number of clusters of human cases and deaths were discovered, particularly in Indonesia, Thailand, Turkey and Vietnam. On the surface it would seem that some of these could well have been human-to-human infections. All these clusters were among family members or nurses who were in long, close contact with patients. Probably the critical variable was viral load and continued exposure to infectious patients in a restricted living and sleeping space.

Much was also made of the fact that it had been some time since the last human pandemic of influenza and that the world was overdue for another pandemic and many argued that it was just a matter of time (see e.g. Germann et.al, 2006, and Longini, 2005). The history of pandemics over the last three centuries reveals the spacing between such events to have varied from five to 53 years (see Figure 7.3). In 2005 we did not know when the next pandemic might occur, let alone whether or not it might be mild or severe. In 2005 no one could foresee that within four years the world would experience the first influenza pandemic in 40 years. Of the three influenza pandemics to have occurred last century, two were mild and traditionally affected the elderly, while one was particularly severe. The 1918-19 pandemic was probably unique in its severity and that it largely targeted young healthy adults.

By the beginning of 2013, 622 people had been infected with Avian flu and there had been 371 deaths, the majority in Vietnam and Indonesia (WHO, 2013, p.1). The first association of H5N1 with human cases occurred in Hong Kong in 1997 when there were 18 cases and six deaths. All these cases were closely associated with an outbreak of avian flu centred on the live bird market. The risk of human infection, then and now, seemed almost exclusively related to direct and close exposure to diseased birds via the medium of infected droppings in water or on surfaces, sleeping in the same room as infected birds, or exposure during the slaughter, de-feathering and preparation of infected birds for cooking. Much was also made of the virus's ability to infect a wide range of bird species as well as to jump to other mammal species such as cats, pigs and tigers. At the time, conclusive evidence was hard to find and it was more than possible that such species were simply fed the carcases of infected birds.

The fact remains that the transmission of avian flu to humans during 2005 remained rare. Given that millions of humans had been exposed to the pathogenic form of the virus in the years leading up to 2005, the actual number of cases remained exceedingly low and the virus did not show any ability to jump directly to humans. Many leading flu virologists such as Peter Palese and Paul Offit did not believe that this virus would be the one which caused the next human pandemic (see Normile, 2005, pp.1112-1113). That said, there were some developments which indicated changes in the virus which could make a human pandemic more likely. These included the virus establishing a permanent ecological niche among ducks in many rural areas of Asia, as well as the virus developing the ability to survive in a broad range of environmental conditions. At the same time the virus also seems to have become increasingly pathogenic in poultry.

Since December 2021 Bird Flu has run amok around our world, killing millions of birds and threatening to spread to other animals. This outbreak is the deadliest since 2014-15 and so far has killed more than 60 million domestic birds. In parts of America the virus has been particularly fast moving, destroying millions of poultry and wild birds. By early 2023 at least 65 countries around the world have experienced outbreaks and many millions of hens and chickens either killed or slaughtered for fear of the disease spreading. Currently Japan is battling its worst outbreak of Avian Flu ever recorded with millions of chickens culled. So far Australia has managed to avoid a major outbreak of the virus and if the latest outbreak spreads to involve Australia it would decimate poultry and wild birds. Fortunately, Australia has one important advantage.

Avian flu in Europe, North America and Asia has been mainly spread through large species of waterfowl not found in Australia. But things could change, and it remains possible for the virus to arrive on Australia's doorstep carried by migratory shore birds. Is vaccination an answer? Well, currently the USA and Europe have been considering vaccinating their poultry flocks, something currently carried out in parts of Asia. While such vaccination my offer protection to domesticated poultry Avian Flu could still be spread by wild birds. So far, the virus has only affected a few humans and since the early 20$^{th}$ century around 2,600 human infections have been recorded with slightly more than 1,000 deaths, the majority involving people who worked with poultry or interacted with wild birds. Despite this our concern is that the virus may eventually mutate and/or spill over to infect mammals.

Like SARS and Covid Bird Flu has brought to the fore issues of public confidence as well as increasing awareness of good government, cooperation and accountability. It has also highlighted the extent of poverty thorough out Asia and other parts of the world. The current Avian Flu outbreak is the deadliest in almost 10 years and while infections in humans are rare and so far Australia has remained safe, some people are concerned that the disease could eventually mutate and spread among humans. If this was to happen then it would raise a host of critical problems including the fact that our immune system may have no defence against viruses harboured in wildlife. It would also seem that little can be done to protect wild birds particularly seasonally migrating waterfowl, which transport the virus without being infected by it. A few vaccines are currently available. Andenz was approved in 2020 but Australia has retained only small stockpiles of Bird Flu vaccines and if a major outbreak occurred would struggle with their reaction. There is also the threat that if the disease mutates into new variants, existing vaccines may not be effective and that it would possibly take the Australian Government more than six months to create or access enough vaccine for the population.

## Swine Flu

Over the last few years our world has been transformed by the emergence of a number of 'new' infectious diseases, such as SARS, Mad Cow Disease, Avian Influenza, and now Swine Flu. All have captured the public's imagination and served to focus attention on the fragile relationship that exists between humans and their microbial environment. Swine Flu is only the latest in a growing list of such infectious disease threats and is the first pandemic to be declared in over 40 years.

Most influenza pandemics have had a tendency to unfold in a series of waves, the later waves being more virulent than the earlier ones. During each, intense but sporadic local outbreaks were followed by more lethal second and third waves. In the Northern Hemisphere swine flu followed much the same pattern. In the United Kingdom, for example, a first wave of the virus appeared in July 2009 followed by another in October-November (Figure 7.4). In Australia things were different, and the country only experienced one major wave of swine flu, closely corresponding with the winter months of July- August.

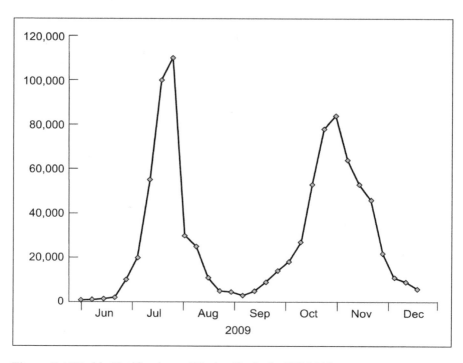

**Figure 7.4** Weekly Notifications of Swine Flu in the UK 2009.

## Where did swine flu come from and have we ever seen it before?

Swine flu or H1N1 is a virus normally found in pigs. 2009 H1N1, however, is a particularly complex virus being an unusual mix of swine, bird and human flu viruses. The current swine flu genetic sequences seem to have originated in two strains, one from North American pigs, and one from Eurasian pigs (see CDC, 2013). H1N1 as we now know it, probably circulated in pigs for years before it was able to make the jump to infect humans, and it probably had been infecting humans in Mexico for some time before it was finally distinguished from routine seasonal influenza. While there is no record of swine flu causing a human pandemic until now, the 1976 outbreak among US soldiers at Fort Dix in New Jersey and Fort Meade in Maryland remains etched on the public health memory. Two hundred soldiers fell ill with what turned out to be swine flu, inciting a wave of panic to sweep through the community. In response, the US Government commenced an expensive nation-wide vaccination campaign. When a pandemic never eventuated the program was halted, but not before hundreds of people had developed the paralysing Guillain-Barré Syndrome as a rare side effect of vaccination, resulting in at least 33 deaths (Gaydos, et.al, 2006, pp.23-28).

## How quickly did swine flu spread?

In March and April of 2009 increased reports of influenza-like-illnesses and respiratory infections began surfacing in various locations in Mexico with evidence that there had been an epidemic raging throughout that country for some months before it was officially recognised. Though Mexican authorities attempted to halt the spread of the new influenza by isolating confirmed cases, closing schools and business, and stopping public gatherings, their attempts proved futile. H1N1 cases popped up with increasing frequency throughout Mexico, the USA, Canada and elsewhere. Mere days after the WHO publicised swine flu's emergence, cases began presenting in European countries – primarily among individuals who had spent time travelling in North America. Following increased surveillance and clinical confirmation, the WHO issued a statement on April 24th informing the world that there had been human-to-human transmission of a new influenza virus of swine origin in Mexico. It was quickly confirmed that the same virus was also spreading in parts of California. By April 27th the WHO had increased its epidemic alert to Phase 4, whereby it acknowledged sustained human-to-human transmission was occurring. H1N1 cases had by then been documented in five continents, and most likely there were cases going unnoticed and undocumented in Africa. Before the month of April had concluded, the WHO had informed the world that there was a significant risk of H1N1 becoming a pandemic. Roughly six weeks later the WHO upgraded the risk to a reality. By that point, 74 countries and territories had clinically confirmed cases. When, on 11 June, the WHO officially declared H1N1 the first pandemic of the 21$^{st}$ century, there were upwards of 30,000 cases worldwide and 144 deaths had been attributed to the disease.

## Who was at risk?

The popular view of swine flu was that on the whole it was a fairly mild infection even though it targeted young people rather than the old. But even today the full effects of the pandemic are still not well understood and it seems more than likely that the official number of cases and deaths is a severe underestimation of what really took place. From the outset the

165

WHO recommended that countries focus on the severe and life threatening cases. In consequence, many cases went unreported. Normally the people most susceptible to influenza are the old and the very young. Only two major flu pandemics have deviated from this trend. As was the case in 1918-19, attack rates with the 2009 swine flu outbreak were highest in children and young adults. People aged over 60 seemed to be the least affected group, with some speculation that this age group might possess a degree of immunity to the current virus due either to previous seasonal influenza vaccinations or infection with the 1918 virus, which was also H1N1 and circulated up until 1957. Despite this apparent degree of immunity, those over 60 who did become infected experienced the severest illness of any age group, with relatively high mortality rates.

In Europe the median age of those infected was 25, and nearly 80 percent of all cases were under 30 years of age, the majority aged between 10 and 19 years. The groups experiencing the most severe illness and highest death rates were those suffering from underlying chronic disease conditions as well as pregnant women and children under two years of age. In Mexico, almost 50 percent of all cases were aged between 10 and 29 years and almost 77 percent under 30 (SALUD, 2009). Though young people and pregnant women were shown to be the most at risk, swine flu affected males and females from all age groups. It would also seem that certain minority and indigenous groups suffered heavily during the pandemic. In Australia, for example, 13 percent of all cases were Aboriginal (DOHA, 2009). The hospitalisation rate for Australian Aboriginals suffering from swine flu was almost eight times higher than that for non-Aboriginal groups and the death rate four times higher. Such a disparity would seem related to the higher prevalence of chronic health conditions among Aboriginals that would predispose them to respiratory complications as well as to poor living conditions and restricted access to health care (See Ruche, et.al. 2009, p.3).

## What has been the impact of swine flu?

It is difficult to truly know the extent and impact of the 2009 H1N1 virus. The symptoms of the 2009 H1N1 virus were not easily distinguishable from those of seasonal influenza, or a variety of other illnesses. Moreover, not everyone afflicted with swine flu sought medical attention and thus received clinical confirmation of their illness. Indeed, for much of the developing world, basic medical attention was not available, let alone the capacity to test for and document cases of H1N1.

The WHO estimates of cases and deaths from swine flu have been largely shown to be a severe underestimation. A recent study states that swine flu may have claimed up to 294,500 deaths worldwide, 15 times more than the figure claimed by the WHO. Fifty-one percent of all these deaths are estimated to have occurred in Southeast Asia and Africa (Dawood, et.al, 2012, pp.687-695). Between April 2009 and April 2010, 20 percent of the US population or 61 million people probably had swine flu, including 26 percent of all children aged under 17 years (CDC, Updated Estimates, 2010). In Australia there were 37,676 cases of swine flu officially declared by the beginning of February 2010, with more than 5,000 hospital admissions, and 191 deaths (*Swine Flu News*, Counts and Updates, 2010).

Regarding swine flu's impact on health care systems, all countries were hit hard for a brief and intense period of time during which many reported shortages of healthcare workers, hospital beds and respirators, which were necessary for those most severely suffering from acute respiratory infections. Though some have criticised countries' preparedness—arguing that the world should have learned its lessons from the near-miss of avian influenza a few years earlier—it is difficult to imagine any country being able to free up the resources necessary to be fully pandemic prepared for the unpredictable 'big one' that might never eventuate. As far as epidemic/pandemic reaction is concerned, many messages emerge from the swine flu pandemic. Most of these relate to pandemic preparedness plans, particularly with respect to what kind of resources are necessary; who should speak to the public; what type of education campaigns are most effective; how to efficiently manufacture, procure and deliver vaccines/anti-virals and ensure adequate levels of public uptake; how many and what kind of healthcare workers are needed and what kind of laws/policies should be considered by governments. Hopefully the world has also learned the dangers of over-prescribing and overusing pharmaceuticals, as now cases of H1N1 resistant to the main antiviral Tamiflu are beginning to appear.

In terms of economic impacts, like SARS and avian flu, H1N1 impacted heavily upon society. Billions of US dollars were spent to develop a specific vaccine, while billions were spent by western nations to purchase and distribute vaccines. It now appears that most developed countries overestimated the amount of vaccination that they would need and that would be desired by their citizens – so much so, that some cancelled anywhere from 30 to 50 percent of their original orders. A major issue here was that by the time supplies of the vaccine became available the pandemic had almost run its course. In order for a vaccine to be effective at the community-wide level, a certain percentage of the population must be vaccinated. With swine flu, by the time that the new vaccine was available publicly, there was already the sense that this novel influenza might not be that virulent. This, coupled with the fact that anti-vaccination special interest groups, assisted by the media, fuelled fears that vaccination might cause Guillain-Barré Syndrome, helped keep uptake rates relatively low, with reports that most countries vaccinated only 10 to 20 percent of their populations. These rates were probably not be enough to ensure community-wide immunity.

In late September 2009 the Australian Government began a large- scale vaccination program against swine flu. By the end of February 2010, approximately 3.8 million Australians had sought vaccination, approximately 18 percent of the total population. Interestingly, at least 56 percent of all Australians did not seek vaccination and had no intention of doing so. About half believed that swine flu presented no risk to their health, 12 percent believed that the pandemic had run its course and almost 16 percent had some suspicions about the virus and possible side effects. Tasmania was the state with the highest vaccination rate (23.5 percent), while Western Australia had the lowest (15 percent) (Australian Government, 2010).

Like all major infectious disease outbreaks, swine flu impacted heavily on the world's economic sector. Throughout Mexico and parts of North America people went out of their way to avoid crowded shopping malls, restaurants, cinemas and railway stations. In Mexico closures and cancelled events cost at least $US57 million a day (Deniz, 2012, p.2). There was a dramatic fall in retail sales and the tourism and travel industry suffered a major hiccup due to cancellations and postponements of trips. Airline shares fell accordingly with British Airways and Cathay Pacific shares down by eight percent and Qantas by four percent. The global meat trade also experienced a decline as people avoided sausage, bacon and pork with some countries such as Russia and China placing bans on the import of such products. As with SARS and Avian flu there were some who benefited from the outbreak of swine flu. Pharmaceutical and drug companies such as the manufacturers of the drugs Tamiflu and Relenza saw their share prices rise substantially.

Although we do not have an adequate estimate of the economic costs of 2009 H1N1 pandemic at present, it is useful to note that SARS was estimated to have cost the Asia-Pacific region upwards of $US40 billion in 2003—and SARS infected and killed far fewer people, though, admittedly, it was a completely unknown disease which instigated a level of hype and hysteria not seen for many years. Interestingly, in early 2010 the German member of the Health Committee of the Council of Europe publically claimed that a number of major pharmaceutical lobbies and governments had orchestrated a "campaign of panic" by exaggerating many normal seasonal flu cases into swine flu simply to place pressure on the WHO to declare a pandemic, thus benefiting the producers of vaccines (See Odent, 2010).

## How did the human community react and respond?

When confronted by swine flu, most countries attempted to delay the spread of the virus by measures of local control. The most obvious mechanisms for doing so included increasing surveillance and instigating wide-reaching public education campaigns, as well as encouraging people to wear masks and avoid public gatherings. In some instances where outbreaks were widespread, schools were temporarily closed and public gatherings cancelled. The experience of SARS made officials somewhat cautious about instituting local isolation and quarantine programs partly because of the ethical issues of infringing individual rights and liberties and partly for fear of the psychological impacts upon those incarcerated.

As with SARS and avian flu, the media played a defining role in presenting swine flu to the public and determining how the public responded to the pandemic and to the advice of health practitioners and government officials. As the pandemic lessened, there was much reflection upon whether or not the media had incited unnecessary public anxiety (Plate 7.1). There was equal reflection on whether or not public health officials communicated with and educated the public effectively. Such post-pandemic reflections are useful because it is important for both the media and the public health community to understand what could be handled differently—and better –when the next pandemic occurs.

## Nations without borders- the internationalisation of infectious disease

SARS, Avian and Swine flu dramatically brought home the fact that we live in a globalised, interconnected world filled with microbial threats that arise in one place, are often amplified by human agency and behaviour, and then move with ease around the world in days, sometimes hours. Human mobility has transformed our world, and the range, volume and speed of human movement has reached levels never before seen. The number of international travellers crossing international borders by air now exceeds 2.5 billion a year and most journeys take far less than the normal incubation time of most infectious diseases. It is not only people that cross borders; global trade in food and other goods has increased more than 25 fold over the last few decades. Infectious diseases seemingly move at will, in passengers, in luggage, in aircraft, in food and other traded goods, or amongst birds in their normal migratory routes. In such a world, national borders have lost their meaning and no longer offer any protection against the invasion of infectious disease, and a disease outbreak anywhere in the world becomes a threat for Australia.

If there is a pandemic of influenza sometime in the next few years, it will operate in a unique environment. It will strike an interconnected world, characterised by unprecedented human mobility, by a globalised economy, and a by 24/7 global news network. SARS was the first epidemic since the advent of the 24/7 cable news network. The ramifications of a pandemic under such circumstances are considerable.

What messages emerge from these three epidemic outbreaks over the last 10 years and are we destined, like our forebears to forget the lessons learned once the epidemic crisis has passed and simply revert to old ways? Critically, we should continue to marvel at the resilience and restless power of the microbial world. Not only do microbes have a numbers advantage, but they are programmed for survival and have the ability to evolve and adjust to any assault that we may launch against them. Influenza viruses are a classic example of this. There is little doubt that we are living at a time of resurging and re-emerging infectious diseases and while we may be better prepared than ever before in terms of medical science, health care, new vaccines, anti-viral drugs and antibiotics, the fact remains that, faced by a viral foe that mutates and evolves from one year to the next, we remain exceedingly vulnerable.

In 2003 a WHO report summing up the SARS experience could write:-

> Around the world, the SARS experience has shown – once again- the power of a poorly understood new infectious disease to incite widespread public anxiety, and fear of SARS has spread faster than the virus, causing great social unease, economic losses, and some political changes. Unwarranted discrimination has been another unfortunate problem. In such cases clear, factual and reassuring messages need to be issued by trusted authorities. Panic is fuelled when information is concealed or only partially disclosed ..." (WHO, 2003, p.8). To which we might legitimately add: or when the media promotes anxiety by virtue of sensationalist reporting and/or the use of arresting images drawn from the current epidemic or from ones in the past.

# CHAPTER 8

# COVID-19 Rules Australia

## Introduction

Late in December 2019 a cluster of pneumonic cases of unknown aetiology was reported in Wuhan China. The outbreak was later traced to a seafood market in Wuhan and within months had spread to a number of major cities such as Beijing and Shanghai as well as Hong Kong and then within a few weeks, Chinese travellers had carried the disease to Japan, Vietnam, Thailand, South Korea and Singapore. By the end of January 2020 hundreds of people in China had contracted the disease identified as Coronavirus COVID-19 and within months COVID-19 had spread around our world ushering in our next pandemic. By 2022 our world had been torn apart by COVID-19 and if nothing else, the last four years have demonstrated just how poorly we have adapted to dealing with epidemic and pandemic outbreaks of infectious disease and how we have generally lost the belief that in such times we could simply rely on our governments and the medical fraternity to warn and fully protect us. COVID-19 has revealed that major outbreaks of infectious disease remain an important part of our lives, how vulnerable we remain, and just how poor our current infectious disease surveillance and reaction strategy continues to be. There is little doubt that Australia needs to develop an infectious disease strategy that has the ability and capacity to respond quickly and efficiently to major infectious disease crises.

## Coronavirus COVID-19

Coronaviruses are a large family of viruses known to cause respiratory infections. The Coronavirus COVID-19 that originated in Wuhan, China was a new strain unknown before. COVID-19 is a respiratory infection that weakens the human immune system causing inflammation and commonly leading to a pneumonic and secondary infection. COVID-19 is commonly spread through direct contact with an infected person via coughs or sneezes or by coming into contact with contaminated surfaces such as door handles, tables, windows or public seats. There is evidence that the virus can survive on such surfaces for up to a few days. While there is still some doubt re the infection period it is usually around 48 hours before symptoms appear. Most infected people exhibit a cough, sore throat, fatigue and fever. Most people exhibit mild or moderate symptoms and recover. People at greatest risk are generally those aged over 70 or those suffering from chronic medical conditions. In Australia Aboriginal people also showed high susceptibility.

## The Diffusion and Spread of COVID-19 in Australia

COVID-19 began very slowly in Australia. The first case, a Chinese citizen from Guangzhou was identified on the 25th of January 2020 followed by three other cases among people who had recently arrived from Wuhan. Thereafter COVID-19 affecting Australia was to affect Australia in four distinctive waves (Figure 8.1). The first began in March 2020 after which the 100th COVID-19 case was reported and on the 20th of June the Victorian Government re-tightened restrictions on household gatherings. By November 2020 Australia had recorded around 28,000 cases with over 900 deaths. The greatest impact was felt in Victoria and by late October 2020, Victoria had recorded more than 20,000 cases of COVID-19 and 800 deaths. Within two months, a second wave appeared, first in Victoria and then spreading further afield. This wave continued for almost two months ending on the 26th of August. In total, the second wave caused more than 7,000 deaths in Australia. In June 2021 a third or Delta wave commenced extending for the first time into New South Wales. In late August 2021 New South Wales recorded its worst day with 1218 new COVID cases and six deaths. By the 9th of October at least 431 New South Wales residents had died from COVID-19 since the commencement of the third wave outbreak in June. By the 9th of May in 2023 Australia was experiencing a new COVID or Omicron-19 wave with more than 5,800 COVID cases a day, 2,061 in New South Wales and 1,502 in Victoria to which Queensland and Western Australia added 757 and 639 daily cases (Table 8.1). By July 2023, Australia had experienced 11,700,577 COVID-19 cases as well as 21,817 deaths. Overall, 11,668,002 Australian recovered from a COVID-19 infection.

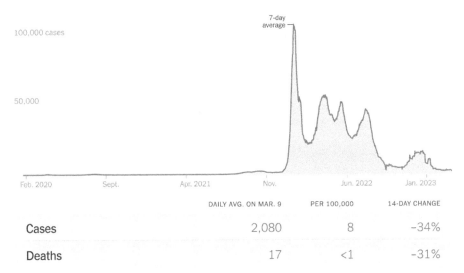

| | DAILY AVG. ON MAR. 9 | PER 100,000 | 14-DAY CHANGE |
|---|---|---|---|
| Cases | 2,080 | 8 | –34% |
| Deaths | 17 | <1 | –31% |

**Figure 8.1:** Daily New Reported Covid-19 Cases in Australia 2020-2023

| Table 8.1: Daily COVID -19 Case Numbers in the Fourth Wave, Australia | |
|---|---|
| **Average Daily Cases** | |
| New South Wales | 2,061 |
| Victoria | 1,502 |
| Queensland | 757 |
| Western Australia | 639 |
| South Australia | 561 |
| Tasmania | 192 |
| ACT | 144 |
| Northern Territory | 28 |
| Australia | 5884 |
| Australian Government, Dept. of Health and Aged Care. COVID-19 Case Numbers 23 May 2023 | |

## The COVID-19 Toll

By mid-April 2023 COVID-19 had produced more than 763 million cases and more than 7 million deaths around the world as well as producing a human reaction characterised by fear, panic and hysteria resulting in isolation, lockdowns, closure of public buildings and shops, cancellation of sporting events as well as a general reluctance of people to leave their homes or go to work.

By the beginning of June 2023 Australia had experienced 11,622,345 cases of COVID and 21,062 deaths. Of these deaths COVID-19 was the underlying cause of 80 percent or 16,810. The remaining 20 percent involved people suffering from some pre-existing health situation and COVID-19 simply contributed to and hastened their death. As Table 8.2 illustrates, the majority of all cases and deaths occurred in New South Wales and Victoria followed by Queensland and Western Australia. As Table 8.2 also demonstrates, Victoria was the State with the largest number of COVID-19 deaths, almost 800 more than New South Wales. The main mode of transmission was through direct or close contact with an infected person or from contact with an infected surface. While there is still some doubt about the length of the infectious period it is usually around 48 hours before symptoms appear. Most infected people recorded a cough, sore throat, fatigue, runny nose and fever. In Australia the majority recovered, although 20 percent of global cases tended towards a severe outcome involving pneumonia.

Not everyone who caught COVID returned to normal life after 3 or 4 weeks. Some succumbed to what is called "long COVID" or "post-COVID syndrome." Long COVID is a broad encompassing term used to describe people who record or suffer on-going COVID symptoms for more than 12 weeks. While there have been limited studies of long COVID in Australia, it would appear that between 5 and 10 percent of those diagnosed with COVID are at risk of having symptoms linger on after three or four weeks. Long COVID symptoms are fatigue, cough, poor short-term memory and concentration. Quite possibly more than 65 million people around our world have experienced long COVID. In Australia it is quite possible that 2 million people have suffered or are suffering from long COVID with some symptoms lasting for more than one year.

COVID-19 deaths also significantly impacted on Australia's elderly population. Table 8.3 shows that 86.3 percent of all Australian males who died from COVID-19 were aged over 70 as were 90 percent of all Australian females. People aged over 80 contributed the most deaths with 64 percent of all males dying from COVID-19 as well as 75 percent of all females.

Australians with pre-existing chronic conditions exhibited a much greater risk of developing severe illnesses from COVID-19. While pre-existing chronic conditions do not cause COVID-19 they increase the risk of complications and deaths. Up until the 31$^{st}$ of March 2023 pre-existing chronic health conditions were reported on the death certificates of 10,850 Australian residents, 80.6 percent of all COVID-19 deaths. Australia's indigenous population had the highest prevalence of chronic diseases such as diabetes, renal disease and cardio-vascular disease and were more at risk of death after catching COVID-19. During the period from 2020 until late March 2023, 33.3 percent of Indigenous people with diabetes died from COVID-19 compared to 15.7 percent of Australia's non-Indigenous population. Those suffering from a chronic condition such as cardiac or dementia who had been exposed to COVID-19 had a greater chance of developing a severe illness in some circumstances resulting in death. Table 8.4 Illustrates the percent of Australians who died from COVD-19 after suffering from a particular chronic health condition. Those suffering from heart disease and dementia made up almost 70 percent of all Australians suffering from a chronic condition who died following exposure to COVID-19.

**Table 8.2:** COVID-19 Cases and Deaths in Australian States and Territories. 2 June 2023.

|  | **Cases** | **Deaths** |
|---|---|---|
| New South Wales | 4,054,502 | 7,026 |
| Victoria | 2,960,087 | 7,830 |
| Queensland | 1,702,385 | 2,991 |
| Western Australia | 1,338,373 | 1,103 |
| South Australia | 919,084 | 1,482 |
| Tasmania | 298,920 | 291 |
| ACT | 241,523 | 239 |
| Northern Territory | 107,471 | 100 |
| **Total** | **11,622,345** | **21,062** |

Data Source: COVID Live, Covidlive.com. 2 June 2023.

**Table 8.3:** Percent of COVID-19 Deaths in Australia by Age and Sex

| Age Group | Males | Females | Total |
|-----------|-------|---------|-------|
| Under 30 | 0.5 | 0.28 | 0.3 |
| 40-70 | 12.8 | 9.6 | 11.2 |
| 70+ | 86.3 | 90.1 | 88.0 |
| 80+ | 63.7 | 75.0 | |
| | | | |

Data from ABS COVID-19 Mortality in Australia: Deaths Registered until 31 March 2023.

In total there were 11,841 deaths of people aged over 70 at the end of March 2023 as well as 9,254 aged over 80.

**Table 8.4:** Percent of Australians Suffering from a Chronic Disease who Ultimately Died from COVID-19

| | |
|---|---|
| Chronic Cardiac Condition | 39.6 |
| Dementia | 30.0 |
| Chronic Respiratory Condition | 17.9 |
| Cancer | 16.9 |
| Diabetes | 15.7 |
| Chronic Kidney Condition | 13.2 |
| Hypertension | 12.7 |
| Muscular-Skeletal Disorders | 6.3 |
| Chronic Cerebrovascular Condition | 4.1 |
| Parkinsons Disease | 3.7 |
| Obesity | 1.9 |

Data: ABS, COVID19 Mortality in Australia: Deaths Registered until 31 March 2023.

COVID-19 also struck most heavily upon Australia's most disadvantaged population where the death rate was at least three times higher than that experienced by the least disadvantaged. Of the total number of COVID-19 deaths until the end of March 2023, 4,272 took place among Australia's most disadvantaged not including another 3,077 in the second level of Australia's most disadvantaged.

**Table 8.5:** COVID-19 Deaths in Australia by Disadvantage Status

|  | **Males** | **Females** | **Total** |
|---|---|---|---|
| Most Disadvantaged | 2322 | 1950 | 7349 |
| Second Level of Disadvantage | 1662 | 1415 | 3077 |
| Least Disadvantaged | 889 | 593 | 1482 |

Data From ABS. COVID-19 Mortality in Australia Deaths Registered Until 31 March 2023.

Finally, Australia's Aboriginal and Torres Strait Islander people were far more at risk of a severe outcome from exposure to COVID-19 largely because of much higher values of socio-economic disadvantage, higher rates of chronic disease and much more limited access to health care. Between August 2021 and the end of March 2023 284 Aboriginal and Torres Strait Islander people died from COVID-19 including those who were suffering from chronic diseases.

## COVID-19 and Aged Care Homes

While Australia generally fared well with COVID-19 compared to other countries, the infection impacted heavily on Australia's most vulnerable and disadvantaged groups. People in Aged Care Homes, for example, suffered heavily in the period from early January 2022 to early June 2023. By the 25th of May 2023 for example, 482 COVID-19 outbreaks had taken place in Age Care Facilities in Australia resulting in a total of 5,507 deaths, 25 percent of all deaths from COVID-19 to have occurred in Australia since the pandemic began. By the 25th May 2023 there had been 139,787 Aged Care COVID-19

177

cases with deaths totalling 5.4 percent of all Covid-19 deaths. COVID-19 continues to play an important role in Aged Care Homes and by the end of May 2023 there were still more than 480 active outbreaks with many Aged Care residents and staff struggling with the disease.

COVID-19 placed considerable strain on Australia's aged-care system. While comprising a very small proportion of Australia's population, residents in Aged-Care Homes made up more than seven percent of all COVID-19 cases in mid-2020. By November 2020, almost one-third of all COVID-19 deaths occurred in Aged-Care Homes. At the end of May 2023 there were 2,755 resident COVID-19 cases in Aged-Care Homes as well as 1150 COVID-19 cases among the staff serving in such homes. The Australian Government eventually issued a National COVID-19 Health Management Plan in 2023 providing a guidance strategy for managing outbreaks such as COVID-19 in Aged Care facilities. The plan called for all Aged Care facilities to put in place a Management Plan to cover major infectious disease outbreaks as well as detailing a list of things that Health Care Providers needed to be aware of and implement to remain alert and respond to COVID-19 outbreaks in their Aged-Care Homes. This included a number of important elements as follows (taken from the Australian Government Dept.of Health and Aged Care. "Prevent and Prepare for COVID-19 in Residential Care," 9 March 2023):

1. All Home-Care Staff needed to be trained in infection prevention and control.

2. All Home Care establishments are required to have a specific Outbreak Plan on hold.

3. A Workforce Management Plan should be put in place during any COVID-19 outbreak.

4. It would be necessary to screen and manage all visitors to the Aged-Care Home to reduce the risk of infection. Those who had tested positive in preceding weeks should not be allowed entry for at least seven days and until they remained symptom free.

5. All Staff should be trained in Infection Prevention and Control (IPC) and all Aged-care Homes should have an IPC Lead Nurse.

6. All Aged Care Homes should establish a Visiting Code to minimize risk.

Many would argue that Aged Care Homes should have had something like this in place at least four years earlier and that had they done so it would have substantially lessened the COVID-19 impact on Home Care dwellers and their staff.

While COVID-19 affected all people in Australia, the young, the old, males and females all suffered as well as indigenous Australians, the rich, the poor and the aged. Over-crowding, homelessness, disability and being very old were all important factors. In all four COVID-19 waves that took place up until the end of 2022 people aged over 80 were the most vulnerable and contributed the most deaths (Table 8.3). In the second COVID-19 wave almost 43 percent of all death occurred in this age group. The third wave was the only outbreak to see more than 53 percent of all deaths to occur among people aged under 80. So far, the majority of deaths during the fifth wave have been concentrated among people aged over 70.

## How Did COVID-19 Affect Australian Life?

From March 2020 many Australian businesses and institutions began reducing services, some embracing full lockdowns and closures, many encouraging staff to work from home. Accommodation and food services suffered heavily with more than three quarters forced to make changes to their workforce. Many sports seasons were substantially shortened and games played behind closed doors. In the second week of March 2020 many Australian institutions and businesses began publicising reduced services and closures. Australia's Reserve Bank cut interest rates and 10 days later the Federal Government announced a stimulus package consisting of a one-off payment for pensioners, veterans, concession card holders and social security recipients. Within weeks State Governments followed suit announcing a series of economic and health stimulus packages. Soon after the Federal Government went further, announcing another substantial stimulus package followed a week later by a Job-Keeper scheme to provide businesses with $1,500 a fortnight for all employees. COVID-19 caused a major change in people's demand and consumption as well as a decline in travel, outdoor dining and recreational behaviour. Such reactions had a tremendous impact on Australia's Gross Domestic Product (GDP) resulting in a large fall during the peak period of restrictions. Overall Australia's GDP is estimated to have suffered a cumulative loss of $158 Billion (Australia National Accounts, National Income, Expenditure and Product. ABS 7 September 2022). By September of 2022 at least one in every four Australians had reported that a member of their home had experienced a cold, flu or COVID-19 symptoms (Table 8.6). This was a decline of one in three in the previous month. As well 93% of all Australians indicated that they had used the RAT Test at home.

Social isolation and loneliness also played an important part in how people reacted to COVID-19. Some of the formal COVID-19 measures had the potential to increase ordinary people's feelings of isolation and loneliness. In January 2021, for example, 36 percent of people reported feeling lonely during the past week (Biddle and Gray, 2021).

**Table 8.6:** Percent of Australian Households Experiencing COVID or Cold Symptoms August and September 2022

| | August | September |
|---|---|---|
| **COVID -19 /Cold or Flu Symptoms** | 36 | 27 |
| **Tested for COVID-19** | 43 | 32 |
| **Used RAT Test** | 92 | 93 |
| **Reported Household member Testing Positive for COVID-19** | 22 | 13 |
| **Required to Work from Home** | 15 | 18 |

Source: Household Impacts of COVID-19 Survey. ABS/ September 2022.

## The Government and States Response to the COVID-19 Pandemic

In February 2020 the Australian Government introduced a wide range of travel restrictions. Foreign nationals who had been in mainland China were banned and returning Australians required to self-quarantine for 14 days. In March 2020 the Australian Government formally declared COVID-19 to represent a human biosecurity emergency and on the 20th of March closed its borders to all non-residents and non-Australian citizens. By this date more than 60 percent of all COVID-19 cases in Australia were among people returning from overseas. In late March the Government required all Australian returning from overseas to spend two weeks in compulsory quarantine in hotels all costs met by the States and Territories. Social distancing was also introduced, and State Governments began to close down non-essential services such as clubs, pubs, restaurants and cafes. After the Second Wave of COVID-19 commenced in Melbourne in May 2020, the Victorian Government ordered strict lockdowns which lasted for four months. In late October the Victorian Premier announced a significant easing of all restrictions. COVID-19 reappeared some months later in Sydney in June 2021. In November Australia began to remove many restrictions, although the Queensland Government announced that all unvaccinated citizens over the age of 16 would be banned from entering clubs, pubs, restaurants, cafes, theatres, libraries, museums and football grounds.

## Federal-State Disputes and Battles

Australia has a long history of disagreements and disputes between the States and Territories and with the Federal Government during times of epidemic and pandemic outbreaks. COVID-19 was no different and disputes emerged over State lockdowns and border closures. As well, some State Premiers came under criticism for failing to bring the COVID-19 outbreak under control. In Victoria the Premier bore most of the criticism and was accused of poor planning and implementation. This rolled on for some months with the Australian Prime Minister urging the Premier of Victoria to ease the State lockdowns, and re-open the States borders. In mid-October the Victoria Premier levelled a barrage of criticism at the Federal Government for allowing New Zealand travellers to fly from Sydney to Melbourne without first discussing the matter. A similar dispute simmered between the Queensland and New South Wales State Governments re the opening of the Queensland border. The Premier of New South Wales argued that Queensland's requirement for agreeing to re-open the border rested on an unrealistic demand that 28 consecutive days without any COVID-19 cases would first be required. The situation was not helped by New South Wales threatening to bill all other States and Territories for the costs involved in formally quarantining COVID-cases and un-vaccinated people in New South Wales hotels. The political dispute extended beyond Australia when the Australian Federal Government called for the WHO to launch an international enquiry into the COVID-19 pandemic including the power to investigate the disease's origins and causes. Such a request China reacted to with hostility claiming that Australia was blaming China for the start of the pandemic and a trade dispute between China and Australia followed.

## Vaccination

In 2021 the Australian Government entered into agreements with a range of companies for the supply of vaccines. On the 15th of February 142,000 doses of Pfizer-BioNTech COVID-19 vaccine arrived in Australia and the first doses were administered a week later. Two weeks later this was followed by 300,000 doses of the Oxford Astra-Zenica vaccine. By April 2021 more than two million vaccinations had taken place and within two months this increased to more than five million. By the end of May 2023 more than 67.6 million vaccine doses had been administered since the COVID-19 vaccine program commenced in February 2021. By June 2023 86.3 percent of Australians had received one dose of COVID-19 vaccine but only 21.55 percent had received four doses of vaccine. (COVIDLIVE.com.au).

## But Has Covid-19 Really Left us?

In the first week of May 2023 the WHO declared an end to COVID-19 as a global health issue. But in Australia COVID-19 has lingered on, albeit at lower levels. By the 9th of May 2023 Australia was experiencing around 4562 cases a day, 1765 in New South Wales and 1043 in Victoria.

Australia now is on the edge of a new Fifth Omicron Wave of COVID-19. The number of COVID-19 cases continues to grow with 38,226 reported across Australia in the last week of May 2023. As well other countries such as China have seen a rise in cases since April of 2023. Despite this, China now seems to be treating COVID as a minor infection, stating that the current symptoms are relatively mild. Australia has struggled to come to terms with the COVID-19 pandemic for four years. For those who could remember past pandemics it was like history repeating itself with quarantine, lockdowns, social distancing, masks, workplace and school closures and people encouraged to stay at home and care for themselves. While most people in Australia have been vaccinated against COVID-19, the virus continues to spread, albeit somewhat slowly. There is little doubt that people are now socialising and mixing much more than during previous COVID-19 outbreaks. The current spread of COVID-19 is due to the emergence of new Omicron subvariants. It is also more than possible that the current COVID-19 wave may coincide and interact with the winter influenza outbreak.

## Conclusion

There is little doubt that one of the greatest tragedies of the COVID-19 pandemic was that despite many countries possessing the technology and tools necessary for responding to pandemic outbreaks, COVID-19 still spread rapidly around our world. Globally there was a lack of cooperation and understanding of how to react and respond. The Covid-19 pandemic without doubt, was one of the worst public health threats our world has experienced since the Flu Pandemic of 1918-19 and Polio and HIV/AIDS in the following decades. Many would also say that our world is not yet free from pandemics of infectious disease. In Australia, a 5th Wave of COVID-19 still lingers on particularly affecting the aged and young school children. Threats from infectious disease in Australia are not new. Australia's history is simply littered with major outbreaks of bacterial and viral infections some of which lingered on for many years. Regrettably we seem to have learnt little from our past experience. Border Closures and lockdowns did work reasonably well but all

Australian States and Territories need to better understand just when and how such measures should be applied as well as ensuring that they pursued full cooperation with the Federal Government. All Government authorities also need to better understand how ordinary people react to such measures and how they behave during times of epidemic and pandemic stress. Our history of epidemics and pandemics is also marked by lack of cooperation, over-reaction and antagonism between the States, Territories and our Federal Government. Around our world new viruses are emerging every year and we still continue to underestimate the importance of the biophysical environment. While it is true that we are better prepared to confront epidemics and pandemics today than we were 50-100 years ago, COVD-19 strongly indicates that we still have much to learn about infectious diseases and how they spread and how people react to major epidemics and pandemics. Certainly, global infectious disease surveillance systems are today much more developed with many countries possessing pandemic response plans highlighting things such as surveillance, rapid identification and response, travel restrictions, quarantine and lockdowns as well as maintaining a stock of antivirals and antibiotics. The bad news, however, is that we still tend to underestimate the significance of the biophysical world and the ability of bacteria and viruses to adapt and change to what we might level at them. In addition, as Australia's response to COVID-19 demonstrates, cooperation and response from States and Territories varies markedly despite the Commonwealth's efforts to address the disease outbreak.

COVID-19 demonstrates yet again the importance of the viral world and how devoid our arsenal of response and reaction measures is and just how much we struggle to control and react to epidemics and major outbreaks of infectious disease. As well COVID-19 demonstrates how we continue to fall back on past reaction and response measures such as isolation, quarantine, lockdowns and social distancing as well as the closure of a wide range of public services. COVID-19 also brings to the fore just how little we understand about how ordinary people regard risk in their lives and how they react to and behave during major outbreaks of infectious disease. It also demonstrates how we struggle to understand the importance of our biophysical environment and the role it plays in our lives still believing that we are the dominant species in our world. The history of pandemics over the last 200 years suggests the opposite. Today the number of COVID-19 deaths in Australia now exceeds the 15,000 who are said to have died during the Flu Pandemic that hit Australia in 1919 and there is little doubt that the COVID-19 outbreak remains one of the greatest health crises Australia has experienced over the last two centuries.

# CHAPTER 9

# A Plague of Fear – Epidemics, the Media, Human Reaction, and the Nature of Risk

The course and impact of the epidemic encounters described in this book involved more than just cases and deaths. They, and the measures advanced to control them, often tore at the very fabric of society, bringing to the surface long held fears, prejudices and grievances. In many ways these epidemics were an acid test of human behaviour, offering a unique opportunity for the study of individual and group behaviour during times of extreme stress. Epidemics, then and now, have the ability to act as a form of magnifying glass illuminating social and behavioural patterns that under more normal conditions might remain hidden. The way people react during times of crisis tells us much about the way societies function and are internally structured, and how our fellows in time and space viewed the world around them and grappled with the circumstances of personal crisis.

## Moral Panics

According to Cohen, "Societies appear to be subject, every now and then, to periods of moral panic. A condition, episode, person or groups of persons emerges to become defined as a threat to societal values and interests; its nature is presented in a stylized and stereotypical fashion by the mass media; the moral barricades are manned by editors, bishops, politicians and other right-thinking people, socially-accredited experts pronounce their diagnoses

and solutions; ways of coping are evolved (or more often) resorted to ...
Sometimes the object of panic is quite novel and at other times it is something
which has been in existence long enough, but suddenly appears in the
limelight. Sometimes the panic passes over and is forgotten ... at other times
it has more serious and long-lasting repercussions ..." (Cohen, 1972, p.9).
As Cohen asserted, it would seem clear that moral panics evolve through a
complex chain of social interactions involving a variety of players including,
governments, the media and others. Cohen's concept of the moral panic might
be usefully applied to the history of major epidemics in Australian history.
By regarding major outbreaks of diseases such as smallpox, influenza, polio
and SARS as examples of moral panic we can better understand how social
responses to such disasters are shaped by far more than the simple number of
cases and deaths and the opinion of so-called experts.

Epidemics have two basic dimensions. In the first place, there is the
epidemiological dimension manifesting itself in terms of cases and deaths.
In the second place, there is the psycho-social reaction that the epidemic
engenders, which reveals itself in an epidemic of fear, hysteria and panic and
which is partly (some might say wholly), orchestrated by the mass media as
well as by the official measures advanced to contain the outbreak. An important
part of this dimension is how such fear spreads through the community to
involve and affect all aspects of our social and economic world. While the
direct effects of epidemics in Australian history have often been substantial in
terms of the number of cases and deaths, the indirect costs or psycho-social
reactions, have often been much more insidious, widespread and far-reaching,
often producing wide-ranging effects. In the case of the epidemics examined
in this book the human reactions to the risk of becoming exposed, the fear
of the medium of transmission and the consequences of possibly becoming
infected with far reaching consequences for self, family and friends, by far
overwhelmed the number of cases and deaths. The 1919 influenza pandemic
for example, known to involve a highly contagious disease, spread by
direct contact, with no known treatment or cure, produced widespread and
substantial human reactions and behavioural change particularly in terms of
social distancing, avoidance, stockpiling of food, masks and patent medicines,
as well as producing a fall in work, travel, shopping and leisure activities.

**The Nature of Risk**

One of the major problems that confronted Australian society over the last
200 hundred years in addressing the threat of epidemics of infectious disease
has been the failure to fully appreciate the dissonance that exists between
how experts and ordinary people perceive risk. Risk to public health and

medical experts is a definable, measurable phenomenon, usually established from experience and by statistically measuring and comparing those exposed to an infection with those not exposed, producing definable and measurable outcomes. For ordinary people, however, nothing could be further from the truth. Risk for most people is not in any way related to empirical evidence assembled by experts, but is rather more shaped by personal attitudes and the way people construct the world around themselves (see for example, Furedi, 2002, p1). Risk for most of us therefore remains a social phenomenon, socially constructed, and our perceptions of risk are largely intuitive and emotional. It remains something to be feared and placed at arm's length. Perhaps a part of this was as McInnes states, because "we are beset by risks, including those of bio-terrorism, infectious disease and climate change" (McInnes, 2005, p.11). Yet our increased consciousness of risk would seem more than just the result of an increase in the number of threats that face us and society daily. Nor would it seem the result of our growing awareness of such threats (McInnes, 2005, p.12). Rather, it has more to do with our perception that the likelihood of such risks has increased and what this means for our personal safety and security. There is also little doubt that many of us harbour deep-seated fears about infection and contagion which remain a mix of rational and irrational fears about infectious disease particularly during epidemic outbursts. Assessment of risk, therefore, is multi-dimensional and very much influenced by contextual factors. In the first place, people make judgements about the source and reliability of the information about the disease outbreak. It would also seem that most people remain highly sceptical of the Government's ability to protect them during times of epidemic crisis.

A US survey into public attitudes towards the Avian Flu epidemic indicated that less than 50 percent of those surveyed had any confidence in the Government's ability to handle the outbreak and protect them (see Ipsos, 2006). Such was the case in the epidemics described in this book. Rarely did people have any confidence in what the Commonwealth or State Government did to control the spread of disease. Furthermore, many of the procedures and controls advanced by the Government simply increased community fear and panic and showed a complete disdain for how ordinary people saw risk. Overall the history of epidemics in Australia is one of the endless struggles that Governments laboured under to fully comprehend the nature of the disease outbreak, the dynamics of its spread, and the impact on the community at large. In most cases Governments reached back into the past to resuscitate old reactive measures of controlling epidemic outbreaks, such as increased surveillance, quarantine, isolation of cases, cleansing and scavenging, closure of public buildings and the like. It would also seem clear that ordinary people make value and ethical judgements about infectious disease based on their perception of familiarity with the particular disease, the perceived consequences that could flow from contact with it, and whether such risks are distributed across the community.

Confronted by a disease like smallpox, influenza or polio, our reaction is very subjective and person-centred, placing emphasis on self and immediate family. In such a context people are also very influenced by the opinions, emotions and behaviour expressed by those around them (see, for example, Hatfield, et.al, 1994). If colleagues, friends and neighbours are fearful then it is more than likely that we will become more fearful. If such people are talking about stockpiling food and medicines, of buying masks and avoiding travel and the local pub, such conversations remain with us and influence our behaviour. Emotional contagion rules the roost and while we do not fully understand the transfer mechanisms involved, it would seem that fear is an emotion that is highly contagious. SARS, Avian and Swine flu provide excellent examples of how fear became highly communicable. People also seem to perceive some disease outbreaks as being personally more threatening than some of the day-to-day risks that confront us. In Australia, for example, the chance of being injured in a motor vehicle accident was far higher than the risk of catching SARS or Avian flu yet in the fear and emotion stakes SARS and Avian flu won hands down.

It is also interesting that our response to epidemics of infectious disease is often not related to the actual severity of the disease in terms of cases and deaths but more related to deep-seated emotive reactions evoked by the particular disease agent. Witness the reaction to the plague epidemics in Sydney and New South Wales between 1900 and 1910 when the number of cases and deaths was very small but the amount of human fear and reaction immense by comparison. The mere mention of the word *"Plague"* was enough to produce an outpouring of human emotion and fear. *"Plague Fear"* may indeed be one of the most basic of all fears, deeply entrenched in the human psyche and nurtured over generations by a mixture of concerns about personal risk, exposure and consequences. Is it possible that *"Plague Fear" was* something that could be passed down from generation to generation in Australia and that the experience of such a traumatic encounter, the emotion and fear that it engendered, went a long way to influence or indeed meld the attitudes and behaviour of subsequent generations? More than 50 years ago Langer argued that it seemed more than possible that children having experienced the fear and terror of their parents and the panic of the community would react to succeeding epidemics in a similar but more intense and aggravated manner (Langer, 1958, pp.299-300).

In the context of the epidemic disasters examined in this book, the epidemic of fear that accompanied each disease outbreak had a number of striking characteristics. In the first place, fear was closely allied to suspicion. There was fear of catching the disease in question and an underlying suspicion that someone close or nearby was already infected and could easily pass it on. In the second place, there was widespread fear about just how the infection might be spread, whether it is by coughing and sneezing, in water and /or food, or by close personal contact. Thirdly, fear and suspicion could very easily be transformed into stigmatisation, whereby people thought of somehow being responsible for the introduction and/or spread of the disease, could be targeted and subjected to abuse. Finally, there was the media who by dint of their approach could engender fear and anxiety.

SARS provided an example of the role fear plays in our reaction to epidemics and how we project our fears and emotions onto a wider canvas. SARS also showed just how badly we deal with uncertainty in our lives and how perceptions of risk and exposure are strongly influenced by our personal experience, our familiarity with a particular disease, and by the opinions and behaviour of people around us. SARS raised a number of important questions about subjective security and what constitutes "reasonable fear". But how much fear is healthy and how can it aid in the prevention and containment of epidemics? Does fear encourage people to undertake reasonable avoidance and control strategies to manage their personal risk and security? Faced by a wide variety of threats, which should we be most afraid of, and can we always rely on Governments to inform and protect us? These are all critical questions which go to the very heart of human behaviour during times of epidemic stress.

## How Does the Media See and Respond to Epidemics?

It is through the media that most people come to learn of an epidemic of infectious disease. Most of what ordinary people learn about such things comes from the way the media describes the epidemic in terms of language, image and placement. Without a doubt epidemics are the very essence of hard news. In media terms they are "newsworthy" and "great copy". They often involve ordinary people with whom we can identify and they invoke and hold human interest by presenting news as "drama" often involving a certain "fright" factor. As Bonneux and Van Damme have remarked, "In a global world, with global media coverage and competition for sensational news, any hypothetical doomsday scenario … risks unleashing a media storm" (Bonneaux and Van Damme, 2006, p.787). It would also seem that people are more moved by the tempest than the gentle rain and that bad news rather than good appeals and the media simply give people what they want.

The media plays a defining role in helping shape the publics' view of risk, creating fear and panic, attributing blame, constructing heroes, targeting scapegoats, and posing solutions. In 1919 when modern medicine offered no explanations or solutions, the newspapers of the day "directed" many people to popular cures and patent medicines as a defence against influenza. While it is certainly true that the media creates awareness in times of epidemic crisis, placing health and safety on the public agenda, and communicating risk in a responsible manner, it is also true that the temptation to sensationalise stories by providing arresting and dramatic images and startling headlines, is often overwhelming.

An important part of the media's presentation of all the epidemics discussed in this book was the symbolic weight and emotional power of sheer numbers. All the newspapers and magazines throughout these disease crises published daily lists of cases and deaths often listing suburbs and townships. Such an approach lent an air of certainty and undoubtedly helped induce more fear and apprehension. In consequence, our attitude towards the media remains somewhat ambivalent. On the one hand, while we may value the information, the entertainment value and the immediacy of news reports and often delight in the imagery, deep down we often remain somewhat wary of the power that the media wields over us. We feel uneasy about the way the media can stir up our emotions by focusing on a particular issue, by ratcheting up the imagery, and by making each story more sensational than the last. Perhaps a part of this is that we derive a certain pleasure from looking at things which in themselves we fear and find threatening. Perhaps fear plays an important role in our lives as a coping mechanism encouraging us to consider precautionary measures and more responsible behaviour when faced by epidemic crisis. Perhaps there is something called "reasonable fear" widely promoted by Government and health authorities as a means of promoting responsible vigilance and preparedness in times of epidemic crisis. Does fear serve the purpose of helping desensitise our attitude towards death and disease? Perhaps as Wilson said, we need fear and welcome it, even though we may deep down hate it, because fear helps us really see (Wilson, 2003, p.456).

Fear has also gained ground as a pleasure or a diversion, a symptom perhaps of modern life where representations of fear play a part in our entertainment. Witness the number of TV and film shows that conjure up the terrors of contagion, pandemics, plague, vampires and ghouls. Perhaps seeing the endless repetition of such things creates a degree of familiarity and pleasure. We enjoy looking at things which in themselves would be threatening and painful to personally experience. It is as if we get delight from the representation of fear. All this the media knows too well and simply delivers us what we want. Fear of fear and the challenge of how to communicate the risk of infection without raising undue alarm may also lead government officials and medical advisors to fall back on secrecy and mis-communication. This took place in China in the early days of the SARS epidemic and also in the UK during the BSE epidemic for fear of the publics' ability to handle such information.

## Mediated Panic – the Media's Role in Promoting Precautionary Behaviour or Instilling Fear: the Case of Avian Flu

The way the media presented Avian flu to the public undoubtedly hindered the rational assessment of true risk. Generally, it is not the responsibility of the media to consider or assess the effects that their coverage of particular events might have on the public. Be that as it may, the behaviour and preoccupations of the media often play a defining role. Avian flu was presented as an apocalyptic event via the media's use of language, image, headline and placement in presenting stories and news items to the general public. In addition, the media's ability to make each subsequent story more sensational than the previous one undoubtedly heightened public reaction. With respect to Avian flu, conflicting comments from Government, world authorities and experts added to the general confusion, and increased public apprehension and fear. In an interconnected world with 24/7 global media coverage as well as endless competition for news, any hypothetical pandemic that threatened Armageddon, runs the risk of unleashing a media storm. SARS was a good example and Avian flu followed the same pattern. International authorities and so-called experts also played an important part in fuelling the media frenzy, vying for attention and research funding with spectacular claims of millions of possible deaths, hundreds of millions of cases, and cataclysmic impacts on society.

Overall, the media's coverage of Avian flu progressed through a number of stages over the course of the epidemic. Initially, the media largely pursued a "watching brief" on the Asian situation with articles adopting an "are we ready" approach. By late 2004 as the crisis unfolded, a more ominous tone emerged. Avian flu was now *"a ticking time bomb"* and a *"monster in the making"*. In the first few months of 2005 *"health chiefs were warning of a deadly flu"*, Avian flu was becoming *"the next global pandemic"* and infected birds *"the most dangerous creatures on earth"*. In the second half of 2005 media interest developed into a frenzy of sensationalist reporting and imagery. *The Wall Street Journal*, for example, could claim in August that wild birds *"will become the epidemiological equivalent of intercontinental ballistic missiles, capable of eluding even the strictest quarantine measures..."* (Zamiska, 2005). Over the next few months, military metaphors reached their height. Avian flu was now a *"security challenge"*, Australia was "facing an *"invasion"*, and a *"ticking time bomb"* against which we needed to *"boost our defences"* and *"organise our flu fighters"* to confront *"a war and a mystery"*, producing our *"emergency plans"* and assembling a *"new array of weapons"*.

Even this paled with what was to come in September and October 2005 when media reporting adopted a wide range of avian metaphors and sensational imagery. Now Avian flu was seen as a *"killer on the wing"*, a *"pandemic on the wing"*, *"wings across the world"*, a *"virus of our hatching"*, and a *"virus that was spreading its wings"*. Unease was expressed over *"bird flu's pecking order"*, and concern over what might happen *"if chickens came home to roost"*. All of this was accompanied by vivid and sensational visual images of health and other workers in special kits with masks and goggles removing thousands of dead birds. At the same time the media devoted considerable attention to how ill-prepared we were for a possible pandemic, the inevitability of which was taken for granted. An important part of the media's approach was to draw comparisons with what happened during the influenza pandemic of 1918-19. Specific response and containment measures such as quarantine, border controls, anti-viral drugs and possible vaccines were widely canvassed and we were inundated with stories about how Avian flu *"would overwhelm our hospitals"*, the difficulties of mass vaccination and the need for Governments to stockpile anti-viral drugs.

During late September and throughout the next two months the world's media became totally obsessed with stories about Avian flu and the possibility of a human pandemic. In Australia the major newspapers carried more than 800 stories about Avian Flu during October alone (Figure 9.1), including double page spreads such as in *The Sydney Morning Herald* Weekend Edition of 22/23 October 2005, as well as many single page stories. As well, many weekly and monthly magazines, such as The *National Geographic*, the *New Scientist, Nature, Time, Newsweek, BBC Focus, The Listener* and *The Bulletin* ran major articles, and most radio and TV stations carried pieces by "experts".

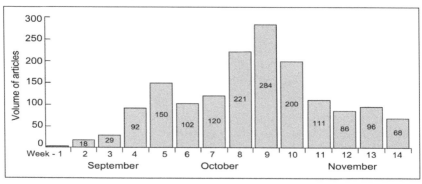

**Figure 9.1** Avian Flu Articles in the Australian Press, September- November 2005

Epidemics, the Media, Human Reaction, and the Nature of Risk

In the last three weeks of October, Avian Flu ranked among the top 10 media stories of the week in Australia. *"The Battle to Beat the Flu"* was the biggest story of the week ending the 28th of October 2005 in Australia. All this news coverage made Avian flu appear far more threatening, contagious and dangerous, than it really was. There would seem little doubt that such media attention raised public concerns about a potential human pandemic. One manifestation of this was a surge of demand by the public for anti-viral drugs such as Tamiflu and Relenza. This was evidenced by a substantial increase in the number of scripts being written by Australian General Practitioners for the two drugs during September and October (Figure 9.2). Much the same happened in other countries such as the USA where there was a noticeable surge in anti-viral prescriptions in New York City during October 2005. In Australia, many people apparently used the excuse that they were travelling to Asia and hence needed a supply of anti-viral drugs for personal use. Tamiflu, the drug that received the most publicity re the treatment of flu symptoms had during 2005 and early 2006 very limited public availability in most countries. In Australia, the demand was so great as to force many pharmacies to establish waiting lists. It would certainly seem likely that the media campaign during September and October influenced many people to seek anti-viral protection and it may have also directed them towards the many anti-bird flu kits which were widely advertised in the British media including "bio-suits" with latex gloves, alcohol-based hand cleaners and 200 electro-statically charged fabric masks each said to offer 99 percent protection against harmful droplets for a day (see *The Telegraph,* January 23, 2006). In Australia, a company distributed special racks of spikes designed to be placed on window sills to keep birds from settling there.

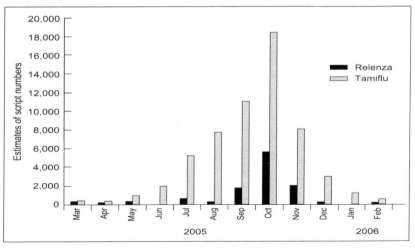

**Figure 9.2** Estimates of Tamiflu and Relenza Scripts Issued September-October 2005.

## Human Behaviour and Epidemics – A Preliminary Model

The psychological climate relating to epidemics particularly the fear and anxiety and how this plays out in our behaviour, tells us something about how particular groups influence and manipulate such disasters for their own purposes. There seems to be a particular socio-psychological sequence of human reaction to epidemics brought about by the official response and containment policies of government and other authorities, by the way the media responds and presents the epidemic to us, and by our own perception of risk, disease and vulnerability. Figure 9.3 attempts to construct a broad structure of the temporal sequence of epidemics within the broader framework of official reaction, media response and human reaction. Initially the reports of isolated cases of disease overseas are largely viewed with passing interest by both the media and the public. The development of an overseas epidemic produces official travel alerts and a move to draft or resuscitate national epidemic response plans. The media too become more involved and begin to draw on past epidemics and hints of what the next one might produce.

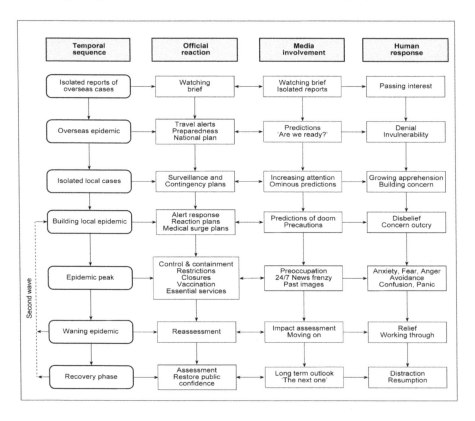

**Figure 9.3** Summary Framework of Epidemic Reactions and Responses.

## Epidemics, the Media, Human Reaction, and the Nature of Risk

The appearance of the first local cases results in the government instituting increased surveillance programs as well as contingency plans and stockpiling anti-viral drugs and vaccines. The media also begin to take a much greater interest with ominous predictions of deaths and disruption. All this ushers in a phase of growing apprehension and concern. When the epidemic begins in earnest and the government issues epidemic response measures, the media engages in a prolonged frenzy of sensationalist reporting. At its peak the epidemic becomes all intrusive, and shock and confusion are linked in such a way as to heighten fear and anxiety. Much of this is influenced by the government's institution of control and containment measures involving restrictions, closures and mass vaccination plans. It is during this stage that the media has its heyday with 24/7 coverage, vivid accounts of past plagues, arresting images and headlines, which while they may inform also contribute to growing fear and anxiety and erode the public's sense of invulnerability. It is during this stage that public reaction can produce such behavioural responses as strict avoidance and aggression towards those suspected of introducing or harbouring the infection and social conflicts tend to be exaggerated and scapegoats sought, while some people seek refuge in popular cures and traditional medicine. All this is greatly amplified by the way the media presents the epidemic news and the official measures advanced to contain the outbreak. In some people this may result in a state of psychological distress as families are rent asunder, neighbours shunned, and normal social and work linkages disrupted. As the epidemic begins to wane and media interest lessens, there is a stage of reassessment and moving on.

# CONCLUSIONS

Threats from epidemics are not new. For over 200 years Australians have struggled to come to grips with outbreaks of infectious disease and to manage the disruption, fear, hysteria and panic that such events inevitably produced. Australia's history is full of examples of such defining events which often played havoc with normal everyday life, and were responsible for producing an environment of fear and dread which at times threatened to overwhelm the country. The epidemics examined in this book were all defining moments in Australia's history. They reveal much about how our forbears regarded the risk of death and disease, how they responded to such events, and how governments and the medical profession laboured to provide explanations and control measures. It remains surprising how small a part our knowledge of past epidemic crises plays in our historical memory and the way we regard risk and vulnerability today. There is also a widespread belief that Australia responded effectively and humanely to past epidemics and that all levels of government cooperated. Nothing could be further from the truth. With the possible exception of HIV/AIDS, State and Federal governments struggled to understand the origin and means of spread of most epidemics, fought with each other, and often produced control and containment plans which did little but heighten human fear and anxiety. We have much to learn from how our fellows in time and space responded to past epidemic crises. Epidemics tell us much about how we manage our lives; how we structure the world about us, evaluate risk and vulnerability, how we are influenced by views and comments around us, and how we react during moments of severe stress. They also tell us much about how our lives are influenced by the media and the way the media responds to such events and presents its news stories. There are many lessons to be learned from how Australia wrestled with the threat of infectious disease.

One important thing that distinguishes the epidemics discussed in this book is that with the exception of smallpox they all remain an important part of our lives and are poorly controlled. It is perhaps a great irony that such diseases remain a continuing threat for present and future generations. Smallpox represents the only real triumph of medical science and apart from some fears about its possible use as a 'bioterrorist agent' the disease has disappeared from our world. Polio once thought to be well under control and close to disappearing, has over the last decade reappeared in a new form of late polio or post-polio syndrome, the causes of which remains a mystery. For the remaining eight infectious diseases discussed, all continue to remain a real threat to our livelihood and public health. "X" Disease, now recognised as Murray Valley encephalitis continues to produce important outbreaks every year throughout parts of Australia. Dengue too, remains a real threat with regular epidemics occurring every few years in parts of Northern Queensland with the continuing threat of the disease and its vector spreading further southwards. And now COVID-19 which continues to linger on. While the impact has been less severe than what occurred in many countries, the pandemic nonetheless drew our attention to many of our weaknesses in our response and reaction.

The continuing persistence of mosquito-borne infections like Murray Valley encephalitis and dengue raises an important issue for Australia's public health. This is, if an infectious disease produces a large number of relatively mild cases but hardly any deaths, then rather than try and exterminate it, we tend to live with it and build it into our everyday life. This is what has happened in the case of both of these infectious diseases. Ironically, if Murray Valley encephalitis and dengue killed more Australians, we would have had a vaccine and/or cure or specific treatment for both infections decades ago. The same dilemma applies to a host of other mosquito-borne infections such as Ross River Virus. While Australia's response to HIV/AIDS has been globally recognised as largely successful, the fact remains that the disease continues to wreck havoc among homosexual men, their partners, friends and relatives. Over the past 30 years some 35 million people around the world have died from AIDS related illnesses and currently there are at least 36 million living with the disease. In Australia more than 32,000 people have contracted HIV since the early 1980s and despite dramatic advances in treatment there still remains no cure or effective vaccine.

## Conclusions

Epidemics and pandemics are recurring events in Australian history. The viruses and bacteria responsible for many infectious disease outbreaks continually change and mutate in ways that make it difficult for human immune systems to adapt or for medical science to provide satisfactory cure or control measures. It is also true that many socio-economic changes are encouraging the appearance and spread of new and the resurgence of old infections. These include increasing personal mobility, rapid international air travel, changes in agricultural practices, continuing modification of the natural environment and the increasing human intrusion on natural disease reservoirs. These and other factors are all creating new avenues for infections to proliferate and spread. But what have we learned from our past epidemic experience? The answer in some respects is very little. SARS and now COVID-19 demonstrate how devoid our arsenal of response and reaction was, and how we were forced to delve back into the past for measures of control, such as quarantine, lockdowns, cleansing and scavenging, isolation and avoidance. And now COVID-19 which continues to linger on and while the health effects in Australia have been less severe than in many countries, the pandemic nonetheless has drawn attention to the many weaknesses in our response and reaction measures. In particular, COVID-19's impact on our vulnerable old people in aged care homes as well as the disadvantaged and indigenous peoples shows how much we still need to do.

It is also clear that during times of crisis ordinary people have little confidence that the Government and/or medical authorities will protect them. Past history suggests that many of the epidemic plans advanced by Governments did little more than heighten public fear and anxiety. The history of official response to epidemics in Australia is also littered with examples of a lack of cooperation, of self-interest, over reaction, and outright antagonisms. In particular only rarely has the Federal Government and all States and Territory Governments managed to agree on how to address new outbreaks of infectious disease. The response to smallpox, influenza, polio and COVID-19 demonstrates how vested interests and interstate and State-Commonwealth rivalries intersected with matters of health, and made the overall achievement and maintenance of public health and infectious disease control a difficult undertaking.

Critically we must also learn that epidemics and pandemics have an important human dimension and are as much psycho-social events as they are epidemiological ones, Regrettably, Governments have not always recognised this. One of the constant themes running through the history of Australian response to epidemics of infectious disease is the failure of governments and medical authorities to fully recognise the dissonance that exists between how "experts" and ordinary people perceive risk, infection, and contagion. Risk to experts is a definable, measurable phenomenon. For the general public, however, it is not related to empirical quantitative evidence at all, but more shaped by personal attitudes and the way we view the world around us. It is a social phenomenon, socially constructed and largely intuitive and emotional.

There is little doubt that people harbour deep-seated fears about contagion which are a mix of rational and irrational fears about exposure, infection and "outsiders" or "others". Fear is an emotion that is highly contagious and we still do not fully appreciate the mechanisms of its transmission, Governments often see a certain amount of fear as a form of 'social vaccine' during times of epidemic crises – something which encourages people to adopt responsible coping mechanisms, but they still do not fully appreciate the role it plays. And then we have the media who in a 24/7 world play an important part in how we view infectious disease epidemics. History shows the influence the media has had on how ordinary people see epidemic disasters and respond. The media's desire to inform is often overwhelmed by the desire to present sensationalist imagery focusing on hidden risks, lurking dangers, disease carrying mosquitoes, fear, panic, flight and potentially disastrous outcomes.

In the final analysis epidemics and pandemics present formidable challenges to everyday life and to Australia's health system. One of the major outcomes of globalisation has been the blurring of Australia's national borders and a shift in human affairs from the nation state to the world as a whole. Fear and anxiety, like infectious disease today, acknowledge no borders and the internationalisation of risks have made us all more vulnerable. How we manage fear during epidemic crises remains as big a challenge as how we control and contain the spread of disease. There is much we have still to learn about the emergence/re-emergence and spread of infectious disease and how people view risk and exposure and how they organise the reality of epidemics in their minds and express it in their behaviour. But there is much else that needs our attention. Without doubt we need to have a better surveillance system that monitors and assesses the significance of animal and human diseases not only in Australia but also in Asia and the Pacific. We also need to better understand the importance of our biophysical environment and how bacterial and viruses rule our world. As COVID-19 has demonstrated we also need to address the vulnerability of those in closed living and working environments, in age-care homes, hospitals schools, shopping malls and businesses. Finally, our most disadvantaged population including Indigenous Australians need special attention during times of risk.

# BIBLIOGRAPHY

## Secondary Sources

Altman, D. and Humphrey, K. 'Breaking Boundaries: AIDS and Social Justice in Australia,' *Social Justice*, 16 (3), 1989: 158 – 166

Anderson, S.G. 'Murray Valley Encephalitis and Australian X Disease', *Journal of Hygiene*, 52, 1954: 447.

Armstrong, W.G. Outbreak of Mild Smallpox at Sydney 1913, Report: Director-General of Public Health New South Wales, Government Printer, Sydney, 1915.

Armstrong, W.G. Outbreak of Mild Smallpox in New South Wales, 1913-1914, Report: Director-General of Public Health New South Wales, Government Printer, Sydney, 1916.

Armstrong, W.G. Outbreak of Mild Smallpox in New South Wales, 1913-1915, Report: Director-General of Public Health New South Wales, Government Printer, Sydney, 1917.

Armstrong, W.G. Outbreak of Mild Smallpox in New South Wales 1913-1916, Report: Director-General of Public Health New South Wales, Government Printer, Sydney, 1918.

Armstrong, W.G. Outbreak of Mild Smallpox in New South Wales 1913-1917, Report: Director-General of Public Health New South Wales, Government Printer, Sydney, 1919.

Armstrong, W.G. et.al. *Report of Director-General of Public Health to the Minister of Health on the Influenza Epidemic in New South Wales in 1919*, Government Printer, Sydney, 1920: 144-181.

Ashburton-Thompson, J. 'Report on Epidemic of Influenza During 1891,' *Legislative Assembly of New South Wales Papers, vol.3*, Government Printer, Sydney, 1892-93.

Ashburton-Thompson, J. 'Guidance of Public Effort towards Further Prevention of Consumption,' Intercontinental Medical Journal of Australasia, IV (10), October, 1899. p.491.

Australian Bureau of Meteorology. S.O.I, Archival Holdings 1876 -, Australian Government, 1912-27. www.bom.gov.au/climate/current/soihtm1.shtm [Accessed: 5 May 2006.

Australian Bureau of Statistics. (ABS). 'Economic Gains and Losses over the COVID-19 Pandemic.' June 2022.

Australian Bureau of Statistics (ABS). 'COVID-19 Mortality by Wave. 16 November 2022.'

Australian Bureau of Statistics (ABS). 'Household Impacts of COVID-19

Survey,' September 2022.

Australian Bureau of Statistics (ABS). 'COVID-19 Mortality in Australia: Deaths Registered until 31 March 2023.'

Australian Department of Health. *Records Pertaining to the History of the Department 1912-63*, Australian Archives, AA 1969/10.

Australian Government Department of Health and Ageing. 2010. *Sixth National HIV Strategy,* Barton ACT: Commonwealth of Australia, 2012-2013.

Australian Government Department of Health and Aged Care. 'COVID19 Outbreaks in Australian Residential Aged Care Facilities,' 4 May 2023.

Australian Government Department of Health and Aged Care. 'Coronavirus (COVID-19) Case Numbers and Statistics,' 23 May 2023.

Australian National Council on AIDS. Infection Control Guidelines: AIDS and Related Conditions. Canberra: Australian Government Publishing Service,

AVERT. 2010. Australia HIV and AIDS Statistics. (http://www.avert.org/aids-hiv-australia.htm. [Accessed: 2 October 2012].

Australian Prime Minister's Department. General Correspondence Files – Influenza, New South Wales 1918-1919, Australian Archives, CRS AQ item 1919/953.

Australian Prime Minister's Department. File of Papers – Influenza Epidemic, Commonwealth Regulations, Australian Archives, AA CRS AZ item 19/1302.

Bancroft, T.L. 'On the Etiology of Dengue Fever', *The Australasian Medical Gazette,* 20 January, 1906:17-18.

Biddle. N and Gray. M. 'Tracking outcomes during COVID-19 pandemic November 2020 - Cautious Optimism'. PDF. *ANU Centre for Social Research and Methods.* Canberra, January, 2021.

Bonneux, L and Van Damme, W, 'An Iatrogenic Pandemic of Panic,' *British Medical Journal*, 1 April, 2006: 786-788.

Breinl, A. 'The Mysterious Disease,' *Medical Journal of Australia*, 1, 1917: 454.

Breinl, A. 'Clinical, Pathological, and Experimental Observations on the 'Mysterious Disease'. A Clinically Aberrant Form of Acute Poliomyelitis,' *Medical Journal of Australia,* 16 March, 1918: 209-213.

Buck, P.H. 'The Smallpox Epidemic amongst the Maoris in the Northern District,' *Transactions Australasian Medical Congress*, 10th Session, 1914: 212-224.

Buckley, C. 'China's COVID Cases Could Top 65 Million per Week,' *The New York Times,* May 29, 2023, 20.

Bull, W.W. *Poliomyelitis in the City of Melbourne*, Department of Health and Melbourne City Council, Melbourne, 1939.

Burnell, G.H. 'The Broken Hill Epidemic,' *Medical Journal of Australia*, 25 August, 1917: 157-161.

Burnet, F.M. 'The Epidemiology of Poliomyelitis with Special Reference to the

Victorian Epidemic of 1937-38,' *Medical Journal of Australia*, 9 March, 1940: 325-336.

Burnet, F.M and Clark, E. *Influenza: A Survey of the Last 50 Years in the Light of Modern Work on the Virus of Epidemic Influenza*. Macmillan and Co Melbourne. 1942.

Cameron, J. Stewart. 'The History of Viral Haemorrhagic Fever with Renal Disease (Hantavirus),' *Nephrology*, 16(6) 2001: 1289-1290.

Cameron, S and Rule, J. *The Criminalisation of HIV Transmission in Australia: Legality, Morality and Reality*, National Association of People Living with HIV/AIDS, Sydney, 2009.

Cameron, S. *HIV, Crime and the Law in Australia: Options for Policy Reform*, Australian Federation of AIDS Organisations, Sydney, 2011.

CDC. 'Updated Estimates of H1N1 Cases, Hospitalizations and Deaths in the United States, April 2009-10 April 2010.' (http//www.h1n1flu/estimates_2009_h1n1.htm [accessed 21 May 2011].

Centre for Disease Control. 'Increased Anti-viral Medication Sales before the 2005-06 Influenza Season- New York City,' *Morbidity and Mortality Weekly Review*, 55(10) 17 March, 2006: 277-279.

Christophers, S.R. *Aedes Aegypti: The Yellow Fever Mosquito*, Cambridge University Press, Cambridge, 1960.

Cleland, J.B and Ferguson, E.W. 'Contributions to the History of Disease in Australia,' *Transactions Australasian Medical Congress*, 10th Session, 1914: 296-325.

Cleland, J.B. et.al. 'On the Transmission of Australian Dengue by the Mosquito Stegomyia Fasciata,' *Medical Journal of Australia*, 2 September, 1916: 179-184.

Cleland, J.B. et.al. 'The Australian Epidemic of an Acute Polio-Encephalo-Myelitis (X Disease): The Clinical Description,' *Report of Director-General of Public Health, New South Wales for the Year Ended 31 December 1917*, Government Printer, Sydney, 1919: 151-153.

Cleland, J.B. 'Epidemic Encephalitis,' *Medical Journal of Australia* (Supplement) 1 March, 1924: 87-88.

Cleland, J.B and Bradley, B. 'Dengue Fever in Australia,' *Journal of Hygiene*, XVI, January 1916: 319-420.

Cleland, J.B., Campbell, A.W and Bradley. 'The Australian Epidemics of an Acute Polio-Encephalo-Myelitis (X Disease),' *Report of the Director-General of Public Health New South Wales for the Year Ended 31 December 1917*, Government Printer, Sydney, 1919.

Cohen, S. *Folk Devils and Moral Panics: The Creation of Mods and Rockers*. Mac Gibbon and Kee, London. 1972.

Commonwealth of Australia. 'Smallpox Epidemic in Sydney,' Parliamentary Papers, vol.3, Government Printer, Melbourne, 1913, pp.1-4.

Commonwealth of Australia, 1920 Official Yearbook, Government Printer, Melbourne, 1919. Communicable Diseases Intelligence. 'Dengue Fever in Australia-1981,' *Bulletin* 1 (23) 1981: 2-5.

Cooper, S and Coxe, D. 'An Investors' Guide to Avian Flu,' BMO Nesbitt Burns Research, August 2005.

COVID LIVE, Covidlive.com. 2 June 2023.

COVID-19 Australia: Epidemiology Report. Communicable Diseases Intelligence, 45, 29 March 2023. www.health.gov.au/cdi: 1-14.

Christophers, S.R. *Aedes Aegypti: The Yellow Fever Mosquito.* Cambridge University Press, Cambridge, 1960.

Crofts, N. 'Epidemiology of AIDS,' *Today's Life Science – Special Issue: HIV and AIDS*, 4(6), 1992: 10–18.

Cumpston, J.H.L. 'The History of Smallpox in Australia, 1788-1908,' Commonwealth of Australia, Melbourne. 1914.

Cumpston, J.H.L. 'Influenza and Maritime Quarantine in Australia,' Quarantine Service Publication No.18, Commonwealth of Australia, Melbourne, 1919.

Cumpston, J.H.L and McCallum, F. *The History of Smallpox in Australia 1909-1923*, Department of Health, Commonwealth of Australia, Melbourne, 1925.

Cumpston, J.H.L. 'Dengue Fever', in Lewis, M (Editor), *Health and Disease in Australia: A History*, Australian Government Publication, Canberra, 1989: 338-240.

Cumpston, J.H.L. "Anterior Poliomyelitis', in Lewis, M (Editor), *Health and Disease in Australia: A History*, Australian Government Publication, Canberra, 1989, pp326-328.

Curson, P.H. *Times of Crisis: Epidemics in Sydney 1788-1900*, Sydney University Press, Sydney, 1985.

Darnton, R. *The Great Cat Massacre*, Adam Lane, London. 1984.

Davidson, G. 'The Recent Epidemic of Dengue in Queensland,' *The Australasian Medical Gazette*, 20 May, 1911: 256-257.

Dawood, F. et.al. 'Estimated Global Mortality associated with the First 12 Months of 2009 Pandemic Influenza AH1N1 virus Circulation: A Modelling Study,' *The Lancet: Infectious Diseases*, 12(9) September, 2009: 687-695.

Deniz, C. 'The Swine Flu's Global Impacts,' www.slideshare.net/ceyhandeniz/the-swine-flus-global-impacts/htm. [Accessed: 19 August 2013].

Department of Health and Ageing. Australian Management Plan for Pandemic Influenza, Commonwealth of Australia, Canberra, 2005.

Doherty, R.L. 'Anthropod-Borne Viruses in Australia, 1973-1976,' *Australian Journal of Experimental Biology and Medical Science*, 55(2), 1977:103-130.

Doherty, R.L. et. al. 'Further Studies of the Aetiology of an Epidemic of

Dengue in Queensland 1954-1955,' *Medical Journal of Australia*, 2 (24), 1967:1078-1080.

Doulan, K; MacDonald, M; Silins, E and Topp, L. 'Needle and Syringe Programs: A Review of the Evidence,' Canberra: Australian Government Department of Health and Ageing, 2005.

Down, I. et.al. 'Experiences of HIV: The Seroconversion,' *Study Report 2012*, The Kirby Institute, University of New South Wales, Sydney, 2012.

Draper, G. *Acute Poliomyelitis*. Nelson, Philadelphia, 1917.

Drew, J.C. 'Epidemiology of Anterior Poliomyelitis with Special reference to the Queensland Epidemic of 1931-32,' *Medical Journal of Australia*, 7 January, 1933: 26-28.

Eisner, T and Ehrlich, P. 'New World Pathogen Strategy Disclosed,' *Science Magazine*, 292, N0. 5526, 29 June, 2001: 2397.

Enserink, M and Cohen, J. 'Virus of the Year: The Novel H1N1 Influenza,' *Science,* 18 December, 2009. (www.sciencemag.org/cgi/content/full/326/5960/1607?rss=1) [Accessed: 17 March 2010].

FAO. 'Update on the Avian Influenza Situation', Influenza Technical Task Force,' *FAOAIDE News*, 33, 2005:1-7.

Fan, E.X. 'SARS: Economic Impacts and Implications,' *ERD Policy Brief,* Asian Development Bank, Manilla, May, 2003: 1-10.

Ferguson, E.W. 'Dengue Fever-the 1925-26 Outbreak in New South Wales,' Report of the Director-General of Public Health New South Wales, Government Printer, Sydney, 1926 :154-164.

Forbes, J.A. 'The Murray Valley Encephalitis 1974: The Epidemic Variance Since 1914 and Predisposing Rainfall Patterns,' *Australian Medical Publishing Co.Ltd*, Glebe, 1978.

Forbes, L. (Ed.). Reporting HIV in Australia: Information for Journalists, *(Fourth Edition)*, Australian Federation of AIDS Organisations, Sydney, 2011.

French, E.L. 'Murray Valley Encephalitis: Isolation and Characterisation of the Aetiological Agent,' *Medical Journal of Australia*, 1, 1952: 100-103.

French, E.L. 'A Review of Arthropod-Borne Virus Infections Affecting Man and Animals in Australia,' *Australasian Journal of Experimental Biology and Medical Science,* 51(2) 1973:131-158.

Freud, S. 'Thoughts for the Times of War and Death,' Strachey, J (Editor), Standard Edition of the Complete Works, Section 14. The Hogarth Press, London 1953-74.

Furedi, F. 'Epidemic of Fear,' *Spiked*, 15 March, 2002: 1.

Gaydos, J.C. et.al. 'Swine Influenza A Outbreak, Fort Dix, New Jersey 1976,' *Emerging Infectious Diseases,* 12 (1) January 2006: 23-28.

Germann, I.M. et.al. 'Mitigation Strategies for Pandemic Influenza in the United States,' *Proceedings of the National Academy of Sciences*, 103(15): 5935-

5940.

Gibson, L.W.N. 'A Discussion on the Treatment of Anterior Poliomyelitis from the Onset of Paralysis till the End of Spontaneous Recovery of Power and Muscles,' *Medical Journal of Australia*, 7 January, 1933: 8-10.

Goldsmid, J.A. 'Some Notes on Dengue,' *Medical Journal of Australia*, 6 May, 1916: 377-378.

GRAIN, 'Fowl Play: The Poultry Industry's Central Role in the Bird Flu Crisis,' February, 2006. (www.grain.org/go/birdflu 1-19). [Accessed: April 12 2006].

Guard, R.W et.al. 'Dengue in the Northern Region of Queensland 1981-82,' *Medical Journal of Australia*, 140 (13), 1984: 765-769.

Gubler, D.J. and Clark, G.G. 'Dengue/Dengue Hemorrhagic Fever: the Emergence of a Global Health Problem,' *Emerging Infectious Diseases*, 1 (2) April-June, 1995: 55-57.

Haefner, D.P and Kirscht, J.P. 'Motivational and Behavioral Effects of Modifying Health Beliefs,' *Public Health Reports*, 85, (6), June, 1970:478-484.

Ham, B.B. 'A Recent Epidemic of Infantile Paralysis,' *Australian Medical Gazette*, 20 April, 1905: 193-199.

Hamlyn-Harris, R. 'The Elimination of Aedes Argenteus Poiret as a Factor in Dengue Control in Queensland,' *The Annals of Tropical Medicine and Parasitology*, (XXV 91), 31 March, 1932: 21-29.

Harder, T.C and Werner, O. 'Avian Influenza' in Kamps, B.S. Influenza Report 2006. (www.influenzareport.com/ir/ai.htm) [Accessed: October 2006].

Hare, F.E. 'The 1897 Epidemic of Dengue in North Queensland,' *The Australasian Medical Gazette*, 21 March, 1898: 98-107.

Harrell, E, 'How to Deal with Swine Flu: Heeding the Mistakes of 1976,' *Time Magazine*, 27 April, 2009. (www.time.com/time/health/article/0.8599.1894129.00.html) [Accessed: 17 March 2010].

Hatfield, E et.al. *Emotional Contagion*, Cambridge University Press. Cambridge. 1994.

Hawkes, N. 'Why We Went the Top in the Swine Flu Battle,' *British Medical Journal*, 10 February, 2010, (www.bmj.com/cgi/content/full/340/feb10_2/c789) [Accessed: 17 March 2010].

Hawryluck, L et.al. 'SARS Control and Psychological Effects of Quarantine, Toronto, Canada,' *Emerging Infectious Diseases*, 10(7) July, 2004: 1202-1212.

Heaven, P. 'Beliefs about the spread of the acquired immunodeficiency syndrome,' *The Medical Journal of Australia*, 1987, 147: 272 – 274.

Helms, K. 'The 1937-38 Epidemic of Acute Anterior Poliomyelitis in New South Wales with Special Reference to the Change in Age Incidence,' *Medical Journal of Australia*, 19 April, 1941: 467-476.

Helms, K. and Willcocks, W.J. 'The 1937-1938 Epidemic of Acute Anterior Poliomyelitis in New South Wales,' *Medical Journal of Australia*, 1, 1941: 467.

Hirschfeld, E. 'On the Dengue Fever of Southern Queensland,' *Intercontinental Medical Journal of Australia*, 21 March, 1898: 143-163.

Holt, Martin; Lee, Evelyn; Prestage, Garrett; Zablotska, Iryna; de Wit, John and Mao, Limin. 'The converging and diverging characteristics of HIV-positive and HIV-negative gay men in the Australian Gay Community Periodic Surveys, 2000-2009,' *AIDS Care: Psychological and Socio-medical Aspects of AIDS/HIV*, 2012.

Hopkins, D.R. *Princes and Peasants*, University of Chicago Press, Chicago, 1983: 287-291.

Ipsos, 'The Associated Press Bird Flu Study,' *Ipsos Public Affairs*, Washington DC. 21 April 2006.

Karesh, W. 'Where the Wild Things Are: The Link Between the Health of Humans, Animals and the Environment,' *Foreign Affairs*, 8 May, 2009. (www. foreignaffairs.com/articles/65088/William-b-karesh/where-the-wild-things-are) [Accessed: 17 March 2010].

Kay, B.H et.al. 'Dengue Fever. Reappearance in Northern Queensland After 26 Years,' *Medical Journal of Australia*, 140 (5), 1984: 264-268.

Kay, B.H. et.al. 'Ae Aegypti and Dengue in the Townsville Area 1982-85,' *General and Applied Entomology*, 19, 1987: 2-10.

Kayal, Philip M. 'Morals', Medicine, and the AIDS Epidemic,' *Journal of Religion and Health*, 24(3), 1985: 218 – 238.

Killalea, A. 'The Great Scourge: The Tasmanian Infantile Paralysis Epidemic,' Tasmanian Historical Research Association. Sandy Bay. 1995.

Kirby Institute. HIV, Viral Hepatitis and Sexually Transmissible Infections in Australia, Annual Surveillance Report 2011 and 2012, University of New South Wales, Sydney, 2011, 2012.

Knibbs, G.H. 'The Influenza Epidemic of 1918-19,' *Australasian Medical Congress*, 11th Session, 1920:321-328

Kumar, Nikhil. 2010. 'Big pharma and the business of HIV/AIDS,' *The Independent*, Available online at: http://www.independent.co.uk/news/business/analysis-and-features/big-pharma-and-the-business-of-hivaids-2147987.html. [Accessed: 30 November 2012].

Lamptey, P. et. al. 'Facing the HIV/AIDS Pandemic,' *Population Bulletin*, 57(3), 2002: 3 – 38.

Lancaster, H.O. 'Epidemics of Poliomyelitis in New South Wales,' *Medical Journal of Australia*, 1, 1954: 245-250.

Langer, W.L. 'The Next Assignment,' *The American Historical Review*, 63(20 January, 1958: 283-304.

Lee, J-W and McKibbin, W.J. 'Globalization and Disease: The Case of SARS,'

Deadly Encounters

*Brookings Discussion Papers in International Economics*, No.156, February, 2004.

Longini Jnr, I.M. et.al. 'Containing Pandemic Influenza at the Source,' *Science*, 309, 12 August: 1083-1087.

Lumley, G.F and Taylor, F.H. *Dengue, Health Service Publication No.3.* Commonwealth of Australia, Canberra, 1942.

Mackenzie, J. et.al. 'The WHO Response to SARS and Preparations for the Future,' in Knobler, S, et.al (Editors), Learning from SARS: Preparing for the Next Disease Outbreak, National Academies Press, Washington DC, 2004:43.

Maclean, F.S. Challenge for Health: A History of Public Health in New Zealand. Government Printer. Wellington, 1964.

Mathewson, T.H.R and Latham, O. 'Acute Encephalitis of Unknown Origin,' *Medical Journal of Australia,* 27 October 1917: 352-353.

McCallum, F and Dwyer, J.P. 'Dengue as a Cause of Death,' *Medical Journal of Australia,* 1 January, 1927: 10-15.

McCracken, K. 'COVID-19: The Australian Experience,' in Rais Akhtar (Editor), *Coronavirus (COVID-19) Outbreaks, Environment and Human Behaviour.* Springer, Switzerland 2021: 173-192.

McCracken, K and Curson, P. 'Flu Downunder: A Demographic and Geographical Analysis of the 1919 Epidemic in Sydney, Australia,' in Phillips, H and Killingray, D. (Editors), *The Spanish Influenza Pandemic of 1918-19*, Routledge, London, 2003 :110-131.

McDonald, S.F. 'Signs and Symptoms of the Acute Stage of Anterior Poliomyelitis in the 1931-1932 Epidemic,' *Medical Journal of Australia,* 7 January, 1933: 1-28.

McInnes, C, 'Health, Security and the Risk Society,' The Nuffield Trust, UK Global Health Program, London. 2005:11-20.

McKibbin, W.J. 'Global Macroeconomic Consequences of Pandemic Influenza,' Lowy Institute for International Policy, Sydney. 2006.

McLean, D.M. 'Transmission of Murray Valley Encephalitis by Mosquitoes,' *Australasian Journal of Experimental Biology and Medical Science,* 31, 1954: 481.

McLean, D.M. and Stevenson, W.J. 'Between Australia X-Disease and the Virus of Murray Valley Encephalitis,' *Medical Journal of Australia,* 24 April, 1954: 636-638.

Meehan, A.V. 'Late Treatment of Anterior Poliomyelitis,' *Medical Journal of Australia,* 7 January, 1933: 11-15.

Merrillees, C.R. 'The 1937 Poliomyelitis Epidemic – Fieldwork,' *Health Bulletin,* No.51, Department of Public Health, Victoria, 1937: 1414-1426.

Metropolitan Citizen's Influenza Administration Committee. Report in Connection with the Outbreak of Pneumonic Influenza in New South

208

Wales – 1919, Sydney, 1920: 1-25.

Miles, J.A.R et.al. 'Isolation of a Virus from Encephalitis in South Australia: A Preliminary Report,' *Medical Journal of Australia*, 1, 1951:799.

Miles, J.A. R and Howes, D.W. 'Observations on Virus Encephalitis in South Australia,' *Medical Journal of Australia,* 1, 1953:7.

Murray, G. 'Dengue Fever,' *Health*, IX (11), November, 1931, pp.105-111.

New South Wales Department of Public Health. Report of the Director-General of Public Health to the Honourable Minister of Public Health on the Influenza Epidemic in New South Wales in 1919, Government Printer, Sydney, 1920.

Normile, D. 'Pandemic Skeptics Warn Against Crying Wolf,' *Science*, 310, 18 November 2005: 1112-1113.

Odent, B. 'Swine Flu: They Organized the Panic, Inquiry into the Role of Big Pharma and the WHO by The Council of Europe,' *Global Research*, 11 January, 2010: 1-4.

O'Gower, A.K. 'Control Measures for Aedes Aegypti. Surveys in Northern Australia,' *Health*, 6, 1956:40-42.

O'Neill, J. 'The Money to be made from the AIDS epidemic,' *The Sydney Morning Herald*, 8 November, 1986: 13.

Osterholm, M.T. 'Preparing for the Next Pandemic,' *New England Journal of Medicine,* 353, 5 May, 2005: 1839-1842.

Paquette, Dana, McEwan, Monique and Bryant, Joanne. *Risk Practices Among Aboriginal People Who Inject Drugs in New South Wales, Australia.* Sydney: National Centre in HIV Social Research, University of New South Wales, 2012.

Perroncito, C.E. 'Epizoozia tifoide nei gallinacei,' *Annali Academia Agricoltura*, 21, 1887: 87-126.

Person, B et.al. 'Fear and Stigma: The Epidemic within the SARS Outbreak,' *Emerging Infectious Diseases*, 10(2) February, 2004: 358-363.

Phillips, H and Killingray, D (Editors). *The Spanish Influenza Pandemic of 1918-19*. New Perspectives, Routledge, London, 2003.

Powell, M.L. 'Symposium on Present State of Poliomyelitis Epidemic,' *Medical Journal of Australia*, 26 February, 1938: 402-409.

Prestage, G, et.al. 'Sex Partying Among Gay Men in Sydney, Melbourne and Brisbane,' *National Centre in HIV Epidemiology and Clinical Research*, University of New South Wales, 2010.

Queensland Branch of British Medical Association. 'Report on the Dengue Epidemic in Brisbane in 1905,' *The Australian Medical Gazette*, 20 November, 1905: 616-624.

Queensland Government. Annual Report of the Commissioner of Public Health to 30 June 1922, *Queensland Parliamentary Papers*, 1922, p. 11.

Queensland Government. Annual Report of the Commissioner of Public Health to 30 June, 1925, *Queensland Parliamentary Papers*, 1925.

Queensland Government. Annual Report of the Commissioner of Public Health to 30 June, 1926, *Queensland Parliamentary Papers*, 1926.

Rice, G.W. *Black November: The 1918 Influenza Pandemic in New Zealand*, Canterbury University Press, Christchurch, 2005.

Robertson, D.G. 'Small-Pox Epidemic in New South Wales,' *Commonwealth of Australia, Quarantine Service Publication* No.4. Melbourne, 1914.

Roe, M. 'Smallpox in Launceston, 1887 and 1903', *Papers and Proceedings, Tasmanian Historical Research Association*, 23 (4) December, 1976: 110-160.

Romanowski, V. 'Genetic Organisation of Junin Virus, the Etiological Agent of Argentine Hemorrhagic Fever,' in *Salvato*, M.S. (Editor), The Arenaviridae, Plenum Press, New York. 1993: 51-52.

Rosenberg, C.E. *Explaining Epidemics*, Cambridge University Press, Cambridge, 1992, p.279.

Rosenstein, S. 'The World is Still Sick of Swine Flu,' *Foreign Policy*, 11 February 2010. (http://eurasia.foreignpolicy.com/posts/2010/02/11/the_world_is_still_sick-0f-swine-flu?obref=obnetwork) [Accessed: 17 March 2010].

Ruche, G.L. et.al. 'The 2009 Pandemic H1N.1 Influenza and Indigenous Populations of the Americas and the Pacific,' *Eurosurveillance*, 14 (42) 22 October, 2009: 1-6.

Ryan, D and Cox, K. 'Lifeguards gear against AIDS,' *The Manly Daily*. 30 August, 1, 1985.

SALUD, 'Distribucion de las defunciones y de los casos confirrados por grupo de edad', situacion actual de la epidemia. *SALUD*, 18 August, 2009.

Scaffer, W.E. 'Vergleichende Sero-Immunologische Untersuchunge uber die Viren der Influenza und Klassischen Geflugelpest,' *Zeitschrift Naturforschung*, 106, 1955: 81-91.

Science Daily. ' HIV's Path Out Of Africa: Haiti, The US Then The World,' *Science Daily*, 1987. Available online at: http://www.sciencedaily.com/releases/2007/10/071029185102.htm. [Accessed: 25 September 2012].

Scott, K. 'The Recent Epidemic of Dengue in Brisbane,' *The Australasian Medical Gazette*, 20 May, 1911: 255-256.

Sendziuk, Paul. 'Denying the Grim Reaper: Australian responses to AIDS,' *Eureka Street: A Magazine of Public Affairs, The Arts and Theology*. Richmond, VIC: Jesuit Publications. 2002. Available Online at: http://www.eurekastreet.com.au/articles/0310sendziuk.html. [Accessed: 25 September 2012].

Shannon, G. and Willoughby, J. 'Severe Acute Respiratory Syndrome (SARS) in Asia: A Medical Geographic Perspective,' *Eurasian Geography and Economics*, 45 (5), 2005: 359-381.

Shaw, J. 'The SARS Scare,' *Harvard Magazine,* March-April, 2007: 48-56.

Sherman, Irwin W. *Twelve Diseases That Changed Our World.* Washington DC: ASM Press, 2007.

Sigma/Swiss Re. *AIDS:* 'The status of the epidemic and possible economic consequences,' *Economic Studies,* 8, 1988: 2 – 15.

Sinclair, D. P. 'The Distribution of Aedes Aegypti in Queensland, 1990 to 30 June 1992,' *Communicable Diseases Intelligence,* 16 (19), 1992: 400-403.

Slavin, Sean; Brener, Loren; Callander, Denton and de Wit, John. 'The HIV Stigma Audit: Community Report,' Sydney: National Association of People Living with AIDS, 2012.

Smith, B. 'The Victorian Poliomyelitis Epidemic 1937-1938,' in Caldwell, J.C. et,al (Editors), *What We Know about Health Transition: The Cultural, Social and Behavioural Determinants of Health, Proceedings International Workshop, Volume II,* Canberra, May 1989, Australian National University, Canberra, 1990.

Smith, R. 'Infectious Disease and Risk: Lessons from SARS,' Nuffield Trust Global program on Health, Foreign Policy and Security. *Risk Case Studies,* London: 1-24.

Stephens, H. Douglas. 'Summary of an Epidemic of 135 Cases of Acute Anterior Poliomyelitis Occurring in Victoria in 1908,' *Intercolonial Medical Journal of Australia,* 20 November, 1908: 573-582.

Sutton, H. 'The Australian Child and the Progress of Child Welfare,' *Medical Journal of Australia,* 11 (20), 1931: 603-616.

Tebbutt, A.H and Helms, K. 'A Report of the Epidemic of Poliomyelitis in New South Wales, 1931-1932,' *Medical Journal of Australia,* 14 January, 1933:43-62.

The Kirby Institute. *HIV, Viral Hepatitis and Sexually Transmissible Infections in Australia: Annual Surveillance Report,* University of New South Wales Sydney, 2012.

Tidswell, F. 'A Brief Sketch of the History of Smallpox Vaccination in New South Wales,' *Australasian Association for the Advancement of Science,* 7, 1898,pp.1058-1066.

Traub, R and Wisseman, C.L. 'Korean Hemorrhagic Fever,' *The Journal of Infectious Diseases,* 138 (20 August), 1978: 267-272.

Ungar, S. 'Hot Crisis and Media Reassurance: A Comparison of Emerging Diseases and Ebola Zaire,' *British Journal of Sociology,* 49(1), 1998: 36-56.

Ungar, S. 'Moral Panic Versus the Risk Society: The Implications of the Changing Sites of Social Anxiety,' *British Journal of Sociology,* 52 (2) June, 2001: 272-291.

United Press. 'Firm Selling AIDS-Free IDs Opens in L.A.,' In *San Francisco Chronicle,* 21 January: 3, 1986.

USDA Foreign Agriculture Service, Thailand Poultry and Products Semi-Annual Overview. February 2006.

Van Damme, W and Van Lerberghe, W. 'Epidemics and Fear' (Editorial), *Tropical Medicine and International Health*, 5(8) August, 2000: 511-514.

Wallis, P and Nerlich, B. 'Disease Metaphors in New Epidemics: the UK Media's Framing of the 2003 SARS Epidemic,' *Social Science and Medicine*, 60(11), June, 2005: 2629-2639.

Whitton, Evan. 'AIDS! THE MEDIA, PARANOIA, AND THE WRATH OF GOD,' *The Sydney Morning Herald*. 17 August: 1. 1985.

Wilson, R. *The Blind Man of Seville*. Harper Collins, London, 2009.

WHO. Severe Respiratory Syndrome (SARS). Status of the Outbreak and Lessons for the Immediate Future, WHO, Geneva, 2003: 1-10.

WHO, 'Severe acute respiratory syndrome (SARS): Status of the outbreak and lessons for the immediate future. Unmasking a new disease.' Geneva, 20 May 2003: 8.

WHO, 'What is the Pandemic (H1N1) 2009 Influenza Virus?' (www.who.int/csr/disease/swineflu/frequently_asked_questions/about_disease/en/index.html) [Accessed: 17 March 2010].

WHO, 'Marburg Haemorrhagic Fever,' *Global Alert and Response*. www.who.int/csr/disease/marburg/en/ [Accessed: 7 July2013].

Wikipedia: COVID-19 Pandemic in Ausralia, 12 January 2023.

Wisher, P. 'Representation of SARS in the British Newspapers,' *Social Science and Medicine,* 59 (12) December 2004: 2561-2571.

Wodak, Alex. 'The Epidemic that Australia does not Have to Have,' *Today's Life Science – Special Issue: HIV and AIDS*, 4(6), 1992: 26 – 30

World Health Organisation. 'HIV/AIDS: Antiretroviral Therapy.' 2012. Available online at: http://www.who.int/hiv/topics/treatment/art/en/index.html. Accessed: 16 October 2012.

Wylie, B. 'HIV and Blood Transfusion,' *Today's Life Science – Special Issue: HIV and AIDS*, 4(6), 1992: 72 – 76.

Wood, James. 'We're in another COVID wave. But it is not like the others.' *The Conversation*, 13 June 2023: 1-7.

Zamiska, N. 'Bird-Flu Hunters take Aim at Far-ranging Wildfowl,' *The Wall Street Journal*, 8 August 2005. (www.post-gazette.com/pg/pp/05220/550637.stm) [Accessed: 10 December 2005].

Zhao, Z et, al. 'Description and Clinical Treatment of an Early Outbreak of SARS in Guangzhou, PR China,' *Journal of Medical Microbiology*, 52, 2003: 715-720.

Zylberman, P. 'A Holocaust in a Holocaust: The Great War and the 1918 Spanish Influenza Epidemic in France,' in Phillips, H and Killingray, D (Editors), *The Spanish Influenza Pandemic of 1918-19, New Perspectives*, Routledge, London, 2003:191-201.

## Australian Newspaper Articles

*Sydney Morning Herald*
'Troopships,' 1 February, 1919, p.7.
'Argyllshire - Eight More Escapees Captured,' 11 February, 1919, p.6.
'Influenza - States Defying Federation - Quarantine Of Troopships,' 11 February, 1919, p.17.
'Mr Fuller indicts Victoria,' 15 February, 1919, p.13.
'Boarding Schools Reopen,' 18 February, 1919, p. 7.
'Border Restrictions,' 19 February, 1919, p.12.
'Influenza Restrictions …' 3 April, 1919, p.7.
'Scare in the country. Experiences of a City Visitor,' 19 April, 1919, p.12.
'Quarantine: State Operations Continue', 7 July, 1919, p.7.
'On The Borders. Many Swim The Murray', 7 July, 1919, p.8.
'Adults advised not to mingle with young people,' 10 February, 1932, p.17.
'Men Blamed for Polio: Sanitary Strike Ends,' 18 February, 1950, p.4.
'Whooping Cough/Diptheria Injections linked to Polio,' 11 April, 1950, p.1.
'Virus spread by flies …' 22 April, 1954, p.2.
'The deadly invasion that can't be halted,' 23 January, 1984, p.12.
'Bitterness of the father of a baby transfusion victim,' 7 December, 1984.
'Aids! The Media, Paranoia, And The Wrath Of God', Saturday Review, 17 August, 1985, p.1.
'Condom Row,' 2 February, 1987.
'This could have been prevented,' 24 February, 1987, p.1.
'Private Blood Bank Turns Investors into Millionaires,' 25 February, 1987, p.41.
'The China Syndrome,' 1 April, 2003, p.1.
'Don't Hold Your Breath,' 12/13 April, 2003, p.53.
'The Cough Heard around the World,' 25 April, 2003, p.13.
'Every breath you take,' 5 June 2004, p.49.
'Bird Flu knocking down Europe's door', 15/16 October, 2005, p15.
'Killer on the Wing,' 22/23 October, 2005, p.27.
'Facing and Invasion,' 22/23 October, 2005, pp. 34-35.
'Rush against Lethal Virus,' 25 October, 2005, p.12.
'Bird Flu on the front line: Race against a lethal virus,' 25 October, 2005, p.12.

*The Australian*
'When Fear takes Flight,' January31/ February 1, 2004, p.1.
'Living with AIDS,' 20-21 June, 1985, p.13.
'AIDS Epidemic could rival the Black Death,' 1 August, 1985, p1.

'AIDS witch hunt: all about Eve,' 9/10 November, 1985. p.1.

'The FEAR of S.A.R.S.,' 5/6 April, 2003, p.1.

'Virus may lurk for Weeks,' 6 May, 2003, p.6.

'Air NZ Clips Wings as SARS Hits,' 16 May, 2003, p.27.

'When Fear takes Flight,' January 31/ February 1, 2004, p.1.

'Grim Warning: Bird Flu could be 1000 Times worse than SARS,' 6 February, 2004, p.1.

'SARS Crisis Cripples Beijing,' 26/27 April, 2004, p.1.

'Pandemic on the Wing,' 9 September 2005, p. 15.

'Bird Flu could involve the army,' 6 October, 2005, p.4.

'The new plague,' 17/18 March, 1984, p.24.

'Vaccine 9 months away, stockpiled shots useless,' 28 April, 2009, p.6.

'We can't halt the spread, WHO admits as more nations list,' 29 April, 2009, p.9.

'Swine Flu capital of the world in Victoria,' 6/7 June, 2009, p.9.


### Daily Telegraph

'Vaccinate, Vaccinate,' 3 July, 1913, p.9.

'Vigilant, Fighting Smallpox,' 7 July, 1913, p, 9.

'Crush at Town Hall …,' 9 July, 1913, p.9.

'Interstate Traffic – Angry Passenger,' 21 July, 1913, p.7.

'Compulsory Vaccination- Meeting in Protest,' 22 July, 1913, p.8.

'Compulsory Vaccination – Why it is Needed,' 23 July, 1913, p.8.

'Compulsory Vaccination – Another Meeting in Protest,' 26 July, 1913, p.14.

'Against Compulsion,' 1 August, 1913, p.10.

'Dr Purdy – Flies as Carriers,' 8 August, 1913, p.8.

'Aids Fear Puts Ban On Phones,' 31 July, 1983, p.3.

'Parents Wont Be Told,' 21 July, 1985, p.1.

'Swine Flu explosion triggers doomsday plan,' 28 May, 2005, p.29.

'Cricket hits out at AIDS,' 26 October, 1985, p.3.

'Rush to buy masks – Bird Flu has US panicked,' 3 November, 2005.

'We can't halt the spread, WHO admits as more nations list,' 29 April, 2009, p.9.

'Treat killer bug with the utmost respect,' 29 April, 2009, p.6.

'Australians will die from Swine Flu,' 2 June, 2009.

'Killer Flu is running wild across Australia,' 29 May, 2009, p.5.


### Australian Financial Revue

'Don't Panic (Yet),' 28 October, 2005, pp.1-3.

***The Sun***

'Don't Panic Over AIDS,' 3 July, 1983.

'Good Services Fight with Scams in AIDS Industry,' 10 December, 1985.

'AIDS TESTS FOR ALL!,' 13 December, 1985, p.1.

## Other

'AIDS FEAR HITS RBT PATROLS,' *The Daily Mirror*, 31 July, 1985, p.1.

'Doctor Blames Media for AIDS Suicides,' *The Advertiser,* 4 February, 1986, p.1.

'The Plague and the Passion,' *National Times on Sunday*. 28 September, 5 1986.

'Mass graves fear in Bird Flu attack,' *Daily Mail*, 1 April, 2006.

## Data Source for Figures

| Fig.1.1 | Cumpston and McCallum, 1925. |
|---|---|
| Fig.1.2 | Cumpston and McCallum, 1925 and Author. |
| Fig.1.3 | Cumpston and McCallum, 1925. |
| Fig.1.4 | Armstrong, 1915, 1916, 1917, 1918, Cumpston and McCallum, 1925, and Author. |
| Fig.1.5 | Cumpston and McCallum, 1925, Robertson, 1914. |
| Fig.1.6 | Cumpston and McCallum, 1925.Robertson, 1914, |
| Fig.1.7 | Cumpston and McCallum, 1925, Robertson, 1914. |
| Fig.1.8 | Cumpston, 1914, Cumpston and McCallum, 1925, Tidswell, 1898. |
| Fig.1.9 | Cumpston and McCallum, 1925, Robertson, 1914. |
| Fig.2.1 | Cleland et.al, 1919. |
| Fig.2.2 | Report Director-General of Public Health, 1917, 1918, Appendix V11. |
| Fig.2.3 | Cleland, et.al, 1919. |
| Fig.2.4 | Cleland, et.al, 1919. |
| Fig.2.5 | Australian Bureau of Meteorology Archives. |
| Fig.2.6 | Miles and Howes, 1953. |
| Fig.2.7 | Miles and Howes, 1953. |
| Fig.3.1 | Armstrong, et.al, 1920. |
| Fig.3.2 | Armstrong, et.al, 1920. |
| Fig.3.4 | Armstrong, et.al, 1920. |
| Fig.3.5 | Armstrong, et.al, 1920, Ashburton-Thompson, 1892-93. |
| Fig.3.6 | Armstrong, 1920. |
| Fig.3.7 | Armstrong, 1920. |
| Fig.4.1 | Cleland and Bradley, 1918, O'Gower, 1956, Ferguson, 1928, Lumley and Taylor, 1942. |
| Fig.4.2 | Sinclair, 1992, Author. |
| Fig.4.3 | Cleland and Bradley, 1918, Lumley and Taylor, 1942. |
| Fig.4.4 | Cumpston, 1938, McCallum and Dwyer, 1927, Hamlyn-Harris, 1931, Murray, 1931. |
| Fig.4.5 | Cleland and Bradley, 1918, Ferguson, 1928. |
| Fig.4.6 | Ferguson, 1928. |
| Fig.4.7 | Ferguson, 1928. |

| | |
|---|---|
| Fig.4.8 | Ferguson, 1928. |
| Fig.4.9 | Ferguson, 1928. |
| Fig.4.10 | Ferguson, 1928. |
| Fig.5.1 | Cumpston, 1989, Helms, 1933, Official Yearbook Commonwealth of Australia, 1950-1963. |
| Fig.5.2 | Cumpston, 1989. |
| Fig.5.3 | Trebutt and Helms, 1933. |
| Fig.5.4 | Trebutt and Helms, 1933. |
| Fig.5.5 | Bull, 1939. |
| Fig.5.6 | Bull, 1939. |
| Fig.5.7 | Killalea, 1995, 1933 Tasmanian Census. |
| Fig.5.8 | Trebutt and Helms, 1933, Helms, 1941, |
| Fig.5.9 | 1933 Tasmanian Census, Statistics of Tasmania, Killalea, 1995, Author. |
| Fig.6.1 | Kirby Report, 2011. |
| Fig.6.2 | Kirby Report, 2011. |
| Fig.7.1 | WHO SARS Report. |
| Fig.7.2 | Australian Bureau of Statistics. |
| Fig.7.3 | Peter Curson. |
| Fig.7.4 | Wikipedia – File Swine Flu UK 2009. |
| Fig.8.1 | Tracking Coronavirus in Australia: Latest Map and Case Count. New Reported Cases. *New York Times*, March 10, 2023. |
| Fig.9.1 | Australian Egg Corporation |
| Fig.9.2 | General Pratice Research Network/Health Commission |
| Fig.9.3 | Peter Curson. |